The Landscapes of Cumbria No. 6

The Smaller Lakes
and Tarns
of Lakeland

Alan Smith

RIGG SIDE PUBLICATIONS

For Kath –
after so many years.

CONTENTS

INTRODUCTION

The last book in this series on 'The Landscapes of Cumbria' was devoted to 'The Big Lakes'. It is now time in this companion volume to turn to all of the other smaller sheets of water in the Lakeland landscape. The small lakes, the mountain and lowland tarns and the picturesque small meres, pools and ponds are just as important a part of this unique landscape as the larger lakes. Many of these have become iconic locations. Tarn Hows, Red Tarn (Helvellyn), Watendlath Tarn or Blea Tarn (Langdale) for example all draw visitors in large numbers. Just like the big lakes they have been painted, photographed, used as settings for novels or poems as well as being magnets for the hill walkers and Lakeland enthusiasts. Even 'tarn-bagging' has entered into our vocabulary for those intent on listing, visiting or even swimming in as many of these stretches of freshwater as possible.

This is a book about the smaller lakes and tarns as part of the landscape. It is an attempt to look at them as landforms; to understand their origins and to explain how they have come to be as they are. It will describe the geological settings, the processes that created these features and the ways they have been evolving and changing. There are a huge number of these small water features – close to two thousand as we shall see in later sections. It is impossible to describe and refer to every one. You will not find pointless lists here, or any inventories of statistics or how to locate them. This is an attempt to explain the different types of small lakes and tarns. The book is divided into eleven distinct sections each explaining the different groups of lakes and tarns in their Lakeland setting.

An interpretation of Lakeland's lakes and tarns in this way has not been attempted before. The following pages are very much a personal view. It may be that I am not seeing things as others do. I have been looking and visiting these lakes and tarns now for many years. I come to it from the standpoint of the earth scientist, curious to understand how such an amazing array of spectacular scenery has come to be arranged like this. A principal aim has been to produce an easily readable explanation of these features. A few specialist terms have had to be used – to help with these a glossary is included at the end. The short list of further reading may help to fill some gaps and take things on a little. The index provides National Grid references to all the lakes, tarns and pools mentioned. The 1:25,000 Ordnance Survey maps are all you need to find them. Enjoy them as much as the author has.

"It was a cove, a huge recess,
That keeps, till June, December's snow;
A lofty precipice in front,
A silent tarn below!
Far in the bosom of Helvellyn"

William Wordsworth
"Fidelity" 1850

Frontispiece: Red Tarn, Helvellyn

6

1. LAKE, WATER, MERE, TARN, POOL, POND . . .

It was a relatively easy and straightforward task to identify the 17 'Big Lakes' of Lakeland covered in the last book of this series. The task now, of defining all the remaining smaller sheets of freshwater that dot the Lakeland landscape presents problems of a totally different order. It is not just the numbers involved (a total not far short of 2000 as we will see shortly) but their sheer diversity of size, shape, origin and location. To add to the problem, they are spread over a huge County the size of Cumbria (6788 km^2) and over the highest ground in England. They are also features that change, as some fill in and disappear, while others are being created and modified by man for a whole variety of uses.

The terminology of how we name and identify this myriad of freshwater features in the landscape also has a certain inconsistency and apparent illogicality. Of the 17 'Big Lakes' already described in the last book, only one (Bassenthwaite Lake), actually had the word 'lake' in its name. All the others were 'waters' or 'meres'. Equally, looking now at all these smaller water bodies there are only two out of nearly two thousand that are actually called 'lakes' – Longlands Lake and Blencarn Lake, both artificial features in the landscape. We use the word 'lake' quite freely, but find it difficult to define. It is somewhat ironic that in an area we call *'The Lake District' or 'Lakeland'*, and where words and phrases like *'lakeside'*, *lake-view', lake shore', 'path to the lake', 'lake cruises', 'Theatre by the Lake' or 'lakehead'* are in common everyday use, we use the word 'lake' so seldom in naming these features. Instead, we have a range of names – arranged in an approximate size order with 'lake' somewhere near the large end and then descending down through 'water' and 'mere', to 'tarn', 'pool' and 'pond'. None can be defined precisely, but all of these names are in wide use. Additionally we have features in the district bearing more local names – lough, dub/dubs, pots, moss or mire.

The word 'tarn' however is far and away the term in most common use, the one most people associate with the small 'lake' in Lakeland. There are over 170 sheets of water in Lakeland that bear the name 'tarn' . . . just over 70% of the all the features that have names on the map. The word tarn is derived from the Old Norse *tjorn* and along with many other Lakeland place names is of Scandinavian origin. The dictionary defines 'tarn' as 'a small mountain lake', beyond that there is no means of being more precise. Attempts to distinguish a 'tarn' from a 'lake' or a 'mere' by more scientific means have all been unsuccessful. In Lakeland, tarns are found both high up in the mountains, but are also spread over the lowland areas. Most 'tarns' are natural landscape features, but several newly created reservoirs and ponds have been given tarn names. Some of the larger tarns are actually larger than some of the 17 'Big Lakes' described in the last volume. Seathwaite and Burnmoor Tarns, for example, are bigger in surface area than Brotherswater or Elter Water. The 'Big Lakes' were identified on the basis of their origin not by their name. They were all **piedmont (ribbon lakes)** excavated by glaciers into the floors of the main radiating valleys of Lakeland. These remaining smaller water bodies are more diverse and varied – best described, in spite of all the reservations about terminology, using the simple terms adopted for the title of this book, of *'The Smaller Lakes and Tarns of Lakeland'*.

NUMBERS

A count is needed of how many of these smaller water bodies there are in the Lakeland landscape and exactly how they are distributed. An obvious starting point is to get out the Ordnance Survey maps and simply count all the blue patches. It becomes immediately apparent however, once you start to do this, you have to make some rules. Do you count every single patch as a separate feature? Or, if you have a group count them as one? In the mountain core of the Lakeland fells and over many parts of the lowlands there are hundreds of pristine, natural features created by the geological and geomorphological processes that have been sculpturing this landscape for hundreds of thousands of years. On the other hand, many features are artificial or have been altered by man's activities in the landscape over many centuries. How do we define 'Lakeland' – are we looking at the Lake District National Park or is it important to look a little wider? How 'small' do we go – are we into garden and farm ponds or should we draw a line somewhere? At what scale of map should we pitch our count? Clearly a sense of proportion has to come into such an exercise, otherwise it becomes a pointless inventory of the ridiculous.

The data presented in Figures 1 and 2 is, I believe, a sensible inventory. The count covers the whole of the County of Cumbria – the widest possible interpretation of the area we call 'Lakeland'. Some figures just for the area of the National Park are there too. This wider interpretation is justified in that the processes of lake and tarn evolution, particularly the work of ice over the last glacial periods was played out over both upland and lowland. The glaciers and ice sheets that excavated most of the upland lakes and tarns in the core of the Lakeland Fells spread out and wasted away over the surrounding lowlands where it created almost as many small tarns as in the mountains. The man-made tarns and pools have to come into the equation because they are features of the landscape. They account for close on 20% of those counted. They are slightly more numerous on the lowland areas and near to urbanised communities, but they are also found in some of the most picturesque parts of the heart of the National Park. Few would disagree with the fact that places like Tarn Hows near Coniston , or Yew Tree Tarn nearby are very attractive spots, but we have to accept that they have been artificially created by man. Very many of the upland tarns have been modified by man for economic uses. Dams have been created to enlarge Seathwaite Tarn and Hayes Water for example. Tarns have been secured by re-enforcements (as at High Nook Tarn), tarn levels have been altered (as at Red Tarn, Helvellyn) and indeed some tarns have been lost by draining or disastrous interventions by man (Kepple Cove Tarn). It is very difficult in some cases to be totally sure whether a feature is wholly natural or artificial. Lakeland is a landscape that is ideally suited to creating artificial pools and ponds. It is an area of high rainfall and of extremely irregular and accidented terrain, just the place where it is easy to trap and impound water.

I first completed the exercise of going over the Ordnance Survey maps and counting all the water bodies in the late 1980's and came up with a total of just over 1000. Since then I have looked over the area again and the data presented in Figures 1 and 2 shows a much more refined and more detailed picture. The initial count in the 1980's was based on the Ordnance Survey 1:25,000 scale maps, most of which were the first in this series and actually dated from the 1950's and 1960's, the then only available sheets. The larger scale (1:10,560, Six-Inch to One Mile) maps of the time provided a little more detail. At present, the newest editions of the OS *Explorer Maps* (still at 1:25,000 scale) show far more detail and pick up more of the smaller water bodies. Features well below about 10m x 10m are shown. The larger scale, newer, metric maps (1:10,000 scale) do not show significantly more water features, but do provide close contouring and other useful topographical details. Comparing the results of the earlier count from the first editions of the 1;25,000 maps and the present day maps it is interesting in that many water features have disappeared in the last 50 years or so, but many new ones have been created. Just as a small example two sizeable tarns on the West Cumbrian lowlands, named on the early maps as Ravelsaye and Sellafield Tarns are no more – the former has gone through agricultural improvements, the latter has disappeared because of construction over the site. Similarly, in the lowland area east of Windermere, Lindeth Tarn has disappeared under a rubbish dump. Tarns that were shown as distinct blue patches on the maps 50 years ago have frequently now degenerated into wetlands with no open water – still on the maps, but not as blue patches (Parl Tarn and Cattlemire Tarn for example in the Eden valley). At the same time there have been a large number of artificial tarns created for a variety of reasons, notably over S. Lakeland (for example in Grizedale Forest or around Staveley-in-Cartmel and High Newton). Far and away the largest and newest artificial 'lake' in the Lakeland landscape is the Wet Sleddale Reservoir, east of Haweswater, created in 1966 for water supply. It is the second largest of all these smaller lakes and tarns and bigger than Elter Water or Brothers Water. Created by damming one of the major radial valleys of Lakeland it is regarded by many as a 'Big Lake' in the landscape. Since the 1980's I have also walked the ground more and had *'Google Earth'* to check out more detail. Walking the ground does highlight the problem and make you realise you have to draw a line in what you record. The exercise of finding every pool, pond, puddle or wet patch just becomes a ridiculous and pointless exercise. On the fells and in the lowlands, temporary pools appear and disappear continuously. If you are not convinced of this, walk somewhere like the summit ridges of Ullscarf, Glaramara or Great How (Eskdale) – count the pools and then go back and count them again on another day.

I am convinced that I have found and recognised all the significant sheets of water in the landscape. I will have missed or disregarded some small features, but they will not be of significance in the wider picture. Producing a detailed inventory of every possible feature is missing the point. I cannot claim to have researched every single one on the ground in detail, but I have examined them all in the National Park and all the significant ones on the lowlands. The aim of this book is to offer explanations of the different types of small lakes and tarns in the landscape, not to produce a list. Most of the obviously artificial features – the flooded quarries and gravel pits, subsidence and mining ponds, the fish ponds and fishing lakes, the amenity, ornamental and wildlife ponds and the numerous small reservoirs and mill ponds do not figure in the story. In some cases groups of man-made pits and ponds, such as abandoned gravel and quarry pits have been counted as single features. Similarly, multiple ponds and scrapes created for bird reserves, or groups of ornamental ponds have not been counted separately. Every single feature cannot be described or listed. The focus will be on how the different types of small natural lakes have been formed. Where particular lakes and tarns are mentioned grid references are listed in the index at the end.

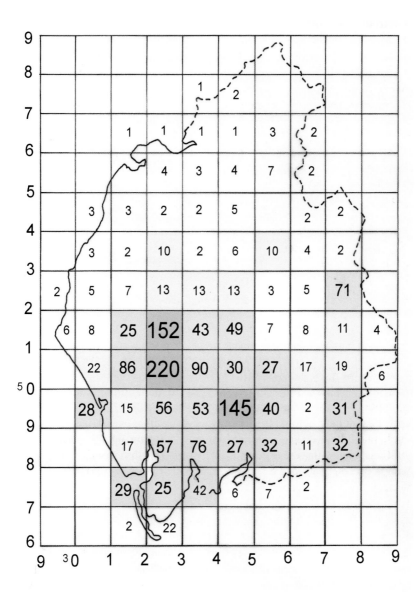

Figure 1. Total numbers of small lakes, tarns and other pools and ponds of all types counted within National Grid 10km squares for the whole County of Cumbria. The three squares with counts of over 100 are picked out in dark blue (Borrowdale 152, Scafell 220 and Crook 145). Numbers are low over all the northern parts of the County.

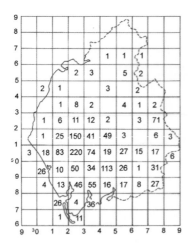 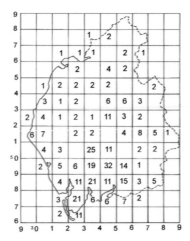

Figure 2. **Above left:** Count of the 1462 Natural small lakes and tarns in 10km squares. **Above right:** Count of the 364 water features believed to be wholly artificial (e.g. Reservoirs, Ornamental Ponds, Quarry Ponds, Subsidence and Mining features etc.)

The data in Figures 1 and 2 show there to be 1826 small lakes and tarns within Cumbria, of which nearly 20% (364) are artificial features. 68% (1086) of the total lie within the boundaries of the Lake District National Park, and of these 167 (15%) have been artificially constructed. Of all the features in the county only 216 have names on the maps and 171 of these have the name *'tarn'* in the title. Many of the unnamed features on the map will clearly have local names. All the reservoirs for example, are likely to have been named in some way by their constructors, but are not specifically labelled by the Ordnance Survey on the 1:25,000 scale maps.

One overwhelming final conclusion brought out by this count and by the maps, is that the distribution of the small lakes and tarns over the county is uneven. There are distinct clusters of features in certain places. These need to be explained. All the northern parts of the county have low numbers of features. The greatest densities are in the higher parts of the central fells (Borrowdale and Scafell areas) and over the south western and southern parts of the fell country. The eastern and far eastern fells have relatively low numbers. The area to the east of Windermere (the Crook area) also has high densities. Elsewhere, the summit plateaus of the fells and moors based on Carboniferous rocks in the far east and south-east of the county (Dufton, Mallerstang and Dentdale) also have many small tarns. Along the narrow lowland plain of West Cumbria, south of St. Bees, is another area of high density with an array of interesting small tarns.

12

GEOLOGY

The underlying bedrock geology undoubtedly goes a long way in helping to explain this uneven distribution of the smaller lakes and tarns over the district. Nearly 70% of these smaller water bodies are in the Lakeland fells based on the old, resistant rocks that form the core area of the National Park. Much more strikingly however, within this area, the different rock types seem to have very profound effects on lake and tarn formation and where they are to be found. Figure 3 shows the geology of the core area of the fell country. Three great bands of old, hard and complex rocks stretch across the area. Over the northern and north-western fells rocks of the Skiddaw Group are exposed with smaller outcrops in the north east and at Black Combe in the south west. These are complex mudstones, siltstones, slates, sandstones and shales, heavily folded, cleaved and much altered by metamorphism from their original state of deep water marine sediments. Across central Lakeland is a wide belt of volcanic rocks - lavas, volcanic ashes and reworked volcanic materials (The Borrowdale Volcanic Group). South Lakeland is underlain by Silurian age sediments; sandstones, gritstones and shales of the Windermere Supergroup. Pushed up into all these rocks are a number of granites (notably the Eskdale and Ennerdale Granites in the west). It is clear that in detail on the ground, each one of these different rock types responded differently to the forces of weathering and erosion that created the smaller lakes and tarns. In these upland areas small lakes and tarn basins were largely created by ice overriding and scouring the landscape. With the 17 'big lakes' described in the last book, rock type was not an important determinant in the distribution of the lakes. They were excavated by powerful valley glaciers gouging out the floors of the major radiating valleys of the district. The glaciers cut indiscriminately across the various rock types, moving outwards from the core area of the fells under a central ice dome. It was the altitude of the central fell area that determined the extent of ice generation and the configuration of the ice streams. Rock type was important only in explaining some of the detailed features of the individual basins and shores. With these smaller water bodies however, the underlying bedrock becomes more important and clearly is a major factor in both their distribution as well as in the details of their shapes, sizes and configuration.

Figure 3 shows the numbers of the various smaller lakes and tarns on the four major rock types. The three major rock bands (the Skiddaw, Borrowdale Volcanic and the Windermere Groups) are not very different in their areal extent, each occupy around 30% of the district. The granites make up approximately the remaining 10%. The numbers of water bodies on the various outcrops however is strikingly out of proportion to their areas. There are only 35 on the outcrops of the Skiddaws, but 715 on the Borrowdale volcanics and

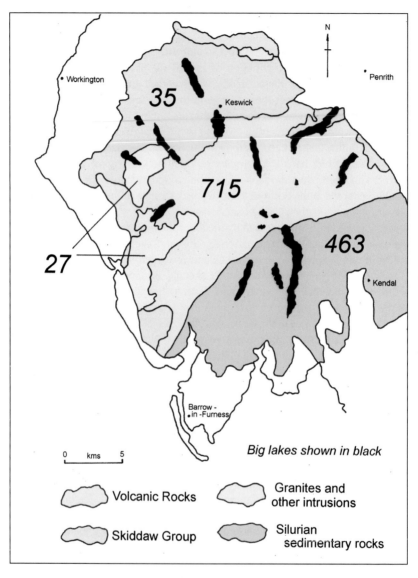

Figure 3. Numbers of smaller lakes and tarns on the four major
rock types of Central Lakeland (Natural features).

463 on the Windermere Supergroup sediments in the south. Lakes and tarns are
also slightly less represented on the granite intrusions with only 27 recorded.
When the individual groups of small lakes and tarns are discussed in the
following chapters the different responses of the local rock types will become
all apparent.

Around two thirds of these smaller lakes and tarns lie in the upland areas of Lakeland – in the core area of the high Lakeland fells, in the Howgill Fells to the east, along the North Pennine escarpment and on the high moorlands of Mallerstang and Dentdale. In the south and east, some of the high limestone ridges and plateaux are also scattered with small tarns. The majority of these features in the uplands owe their origin to the work of ice which eroded and sculptured this landscape in the last Ice Age. At the glacial maximum (~26-14.7 ka.) all the high ground of central Lakeland lay under a thick ice sheet moving off the fells, scouring, gouging and eroding the terrain. Most of the smaller lakes and tarns left in the wake of these glaciers and ice sheets are cut into the bedrock surface, their form and size dependant primarily on the upland topography and the underlying bedrock geology. A few do not relate directly to the erosional effects of the ice, but reflect landscape processes in the 10,000 years or so since the ice has disappeared.

In the lowland areas of the Eden Valley, the Solway Plain, the lowlands of West Cumbria and on the low ground of South Lakeland around Morecambe Bay, ice was again the dominant force in the creation of small lakes and tarns. In these areas ice flows were draining the upland areas, conveying it away into the Irish Sea basin and east over the Pennines. Debris scoured from the uplands came to rest on the surrounding lowlands. Complex patterns of ice melting, movements of meltwaters and different ice flow phases all contributed to the creation of an intricate and irregular lowland terrain. On this blanket of debris plastered over the lowlands more than 500 hollows and depressions of one kind and another contain small lakes and tarns. Many, many more have already filled in with peat, silt and wetland vegetation in the period since the ice has disappeared and many have been drained and obliterated by man's activities. The number that remain are all part of this same story of the affects of recent ice ages on the landscape of Cumbria.

In the remaining chapters of this book an attempt is made to explain and illustrate the range of different types of these small lakes and tarns in the Lakeland landscape; first in the upland areas and then those over the lowlands. It is impossible to describe each and every one. Many are small and insignificant on their own, but are still part of the overall picture. Some do not fit precisely into one group or another, the groups in some cases merge. There are many problematical sites, difficult to unpick and difficult to identify. What follows is a personal interpretation – I may have got some things wrong!

2. SMALL VALLEY LAKES

There are eight small lakes in the heart of the Lakeland fells that are essentially piedmont (ribbon lakes) formed by the same forces that created the 17 'Big Lakes' described in the last volume. They differ in their size and location. Like the 'Big Lakes', they are the result of differential erosion by ice of the rocky floors of the valleys – in these cases by smaller glacier streams in tributary valleys to the major radiating troughs of the district. They lie in enclosed rocky hollows, all in fact excavated into the Borrowdale volcanic rocks of central Lakeland. Some show partial damming by moraines and three have been altered and enlarged to create water supply reservoirs.

Figure 4 (opposite) is a schematic diagram that attempts to put these small lakes into their broader landscape context of the features found in the core area of the high fell country. The 'Big Lakes' of the last volume are shown as A in the figure – major lake basins in the main glacial troughs. These smaller lakes (B in figure 4) occupy tributary valleys.

Hayes Water

This is one of the best examples of this type of small lake basin. It lies in the upper part of the deep trough of Hayeswater Gill, a hanging tributary to the main Patterdale valley that holds the major lakes of Ullswater and Brothers Water. The lake lies some way down the valley from the trough end and has quite an irregular floor, with three distinct deep basins (all over 16m deep) along its narrow length.

Figure 5. The head of Hayes Water seen from Thornthwaite Crag, looking north.

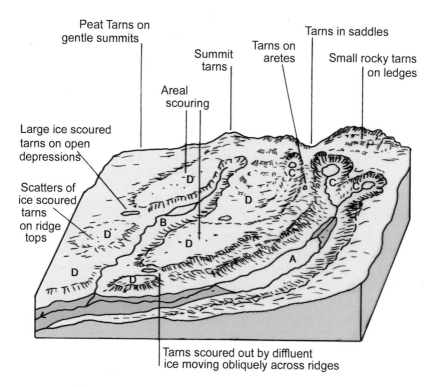

Peat Tarns on
gentle summits

Tarns in saddles

Summit
tarns

Tarns on
aretes

Small rocky tarns
on ledges

Areal
scouring

Large ice scoured
tarns on open
depressions

Scatters of
ice scoured
tarns
on ridge
tops

Tarns scoured out by diffluent
ice moving obliquely across ridges

A 'The Big Lakes' - piedmont (ribbon lakes) in the major valleys
B Smaller piedmont lakes in tributary valleys
C Cirque tarns
D Areal scouring. Tarns and pools scoured out by ice sheets
     moving over ridge and hill tops

Figure 4. Schematic diagram to put the various small lakes and tarns
in the uplands into their landscape context.

The lake has been dammed to provide a water supply for the Penrith district
and now stands 2m higher than its natural level. It has a very stony shoreline
and the surrounding flanks of the lake have a series of very conspicuous,
conical mounds of moraine which date from the period of the Loch Lomond
Stadial (c12.2-11.9 ka.) (Figure 6). A large fan of rock debris is washing down
from a gully south of the Knott (NY 434124) on the eastern side and is
progressively burying the morainic mounds and building out into the lake.
There is also a considerable lake head delta infill. It has recently been
announced (September 2013) that the dam is to be demolished as the reservoir
water is no longer required. The water will revert to its natural level.

Figure 6. Hayes Water. **Above left:** The mounds of Loch Lomond stadial moraines at the head of the lake. **Above right:** The fan of rock debris building out into the lake from the Knott.

Seathwaite Tarn

This has many similarities with Hayes Water. It lies in quite a deep, steep-sided glacial trough between Dow Crag and Grey Friar, and is a major tributary valley to Dunnerdale. It is a very long, narrow, lake contained in a rock basin excavated into the volcanic rocks. It too has been dammed as a water supply reservoir and stands 6m higher than the original lake. The valley is curved and slightly asymmetrical with particularly steep craggy slopes along the SE side. It is a simple rock basin with a single deep point of 29.5m towards its lower southern end. The shore areas show the effects of severe ice scouring. A large *roche moutonnée* feature now emerges from the reservoir as an island close to the north shore and there are a series of ice shorn crags along the south east shore and in the area of the present dam.

Figure 7. Above: Seathwaite Tarn seen from Lead Pike, looking towards the head of the tarn. The curving dam is at the left. Crags of Shudderstone How to right.

Little Langdale Tarn

The present Little Langdale Tarn is clearly what remains of a once much larger sheet of water perhaps three times the size. It is now only 9.5m at its deepest point near the centre. The thick organic sediments on its floor, its shallow reedy shores and the extensive infill of alluvium in the valley floor above the tarn for some 800m as far as Fell Foot Bridge (NY300032) testify to its former extent. Its position where three tongues of ice from Blea Tarn, Wrynose and Greenburn converged accounts for the deep excavation of the valley floor at this position. There is no obvious morainic feature at its eastern end.

Figure 8. Above: Little Langdale Tarn seen from lower end looking up to the Greenburn valley and Wrynose Pass.

Greenburn Reservoir

High above Little Langdale Tarn in the valley of Greenburn Beck lies the now disused Greenburn Reservoir. This is a significant sheet of water much altered from its original state of a rather small valley floor lake, excavated into the floor of this extensive glacial trough on the northern edge of the Coniston Fells. The whole area was ravaged by copper mining activity extending from the mid nineteenth to the early twentieth century. A long dam along the south side still exists, but a shorter feature at the outlet is now breached and derelict.

There are moraines in the area below the present dammed lake but mine working has made interpretation of the original features of the valley very difficult.

Figure 9. Right:
The Greenburn Reservoir seen from Weatherlam looking north. The dam is at the right hand end.

Blea Tarn (Langdale)

The picturesque setting of this tarn creates one of the iconic views of central Lakeland (used in the captions for the BBC *Countryfile* programme). The tarn nestles in the floor of a glacial valley that was cut by a separate tongue of ice moving south from Great to Little Langdale. This is an example of **'diffluence'** (ie. where a glacier cuts across a watershed from one valley to another – Figure 4). Some low moraines along the southern shore contain the tarn. To the north, above the tarn, the wide open peaty valley floor has a considerable infill of morainic and alluvial debris, suggesting the tarn could have been larger at some stage. The tongue of diffluent ice that was able to cut this feature was assisted by faults and weaknesses in the volcanic rocks aligned close to a N-S direction in the upper part of this valley. The tarn is 7m deep with simple basin shape, deepest in the middle and a deep layer of organic debris on its floor.

Loughrigg Tarn

In some ways this has a similar situation to Blea Tarn in that it was excavated by a diffluent tongue of ice moving across a low col in a watershed. Ice from Grasmere to the north overtopped the col of Red Bank, moving SE across into the lower part of Great Langdale. The tarn is circular with quite a flattish floor, 10.3m deep near the northern shore. The margins of the tarn are gentle with grassland, scattered woodland and areas of rich wetland reaching down to the shores.

Figure 10. Above: Blea Tarn (Langdale) View across the tarn with the low diffluence col at the head of the tarn. The Langdale Pikes in background beyond the col.

Figure 11. Above: Loughrigg Tarn. View looking north with Langdale Pikes in distance.

Watendlath Tarn

This too is one of Lakeland's most picturesque tarns, used as the setting for Hugh Walpole's novel *'Judith Paris'* and much beloved by photographers and artists. The narrow Watendlath valley is a classic hanging glaciated trough on the east side of the Borrowdale valley. Its stream tumbles down the Lodore Falls into the head of Derwent Water in the hanging section. The oval tarn lies in rock basin cut into the volcanic rocks. At the picturesque pack horse bridge at its outlet the stream drops steeply down a rocky step in the valley floor. The floor of the tarn is relatively flat in the centre where it reaches 17m in depth. The gentle shores of the tarn are built of alluvial materials and glacial tills and are mostly enclosed as farmland. There is a considerable amount of alluvial infill at the head of the tarn. (Picture on back cover).

Figure 12. Watenlath Tarn, looking north from Watendlath Fell.
Bassenthwaite Lake is seen in the far distance.

Blea Tarn (Watendlath)

Just over 2kms higher up the Watendlath valley lies Blea Tarn. It occupies a rather open basin at the head of the valley on a distinctly higher step in the valley profile, in fact some 215m higher in elevation. It is clearly a rock basin, excavated by a northerly moving tongue of ice that became the Watendlath valley glacier. It could perhaps be regarded more as a summit ice scour type of tarn consequent upon a broader ice sheet sweeping NNW across the fell tops, but it lies in a shallow valley basin and the tarn is aligned along the line of the valley. It has an elongated oval shape and is 13m deep close to the centre. The western shores show many rough ice shorn crags and are scattered with perched blocks of volcanic rock. The eastern shores are covered with glacial till, peat and poor wet upland grassland. The shoreline areas right around the tarn are distinctly bouldery, with much submerged and marginal vegetation in the shallow water. There is no obvious moraine around the outlet area.

Figure 13. Above: Blea Tarn (Watendlath), view from the outlet
at the northern end.

23

3. CIRQUE TARNS

Cirques are one of the most characteristic and easily recognised landforms of glacial erosion. Essentially arm-chair shaped hollows high up on mountain sides, or at the heads of the main glaciated troughs, they are classic sites for small tarns (C on Figure 4). The well developed cirque, with its steep rocky backwall or headwall and enclosing sidewalls, is an ice excavated rock basin. A tarn may be completely contained within the excavated hollow, but is frequently enhanced by a retaining moraine on its lip around the outlet.

The high fells of Lakeland contain around 200 cirque features – some classic bowl shapes, others more indistinct, shallower and less well formed. Altitude, aspect and geology are the major controls on their form and distribution. Surprisingly only 19 of these Lakeland cirques hold tarns at present; perhaps indicative of the relatively few locations where ideal cirque formation was possible in these mountains. Additionally, Keppel Cove had a tarn in it until 1927, when after a period of heavy rain the morainic dam which had undergone modification to use its waters in a complex water management system for the nearby Greenside lead mines, gave way and the tarn waters emptied. There are also very small rather insignificant tarns in Brown Cove (below Helvellyn) and at Foxes Tarn high on Scafell – both cirque features. The tarn in Brown Cove has suffered alteration by damming to provide water for the Greenside mines and is now in a derelict state. Foxes Tarn (Figure 14) is little more than a small pool, less than a metre deep with a very large boulder in it. The whole area is a chaotic rocky amphitheatre dominated by the shuttering of scree debris down from the surrounding crags. Much of the material came down in a violent storm in 1958.

Figure 14.
Foxes Tarn
on Scafell.

Theoretically tarns approximate to being circular in outline in well developed cirques. This is indeed the case with some of the classic Lakeland features. Angle Tarn, Blind Tarn, Stickle Tarn, Levers Water, Blea Water, Bleaberry Tarn, Scales Tarn and Red Tarn (Helvellyn) probably rank as the most perfect examples, and all show close to circular outlines (Figure 17). High Nook Tarn above Loweswater is also close to being circular, but a very low earth and stone embankment at its outer edge is partly responsible for its regular outline. The original tarn in Keppel Cove was also a good round shape.

Figure 15. Blea Water. The most perfect cirque feature in Lakeland. A NE facing deep rock walled basin below High Street with an almost circular deep tarn and morainic ridge enhancing the depth of the tarn.

Cirque tarns characteristically have pudding bowl shaped basins with single deep points in the centre, the result of the rotational action of ice that formed the hollow. Many are deep for their area, notably Blea Water. Five of these tarns are clearly moraine dammed, all the others lie in ice excavated rock basins, with in some cases, moraines playing some part in retaining the waters. The local bedrock geology has a profound influence on the form of all of these cirques. 15 of them lie on the Borrowdale volcanic rocks, and one, Bleaberry Tarn on the Ennerdale Granite. Sculpturing by ice of these massive, resistant igneous materials, with their widely spaced joints and few fracture lines has produced steep backwalls and sidewalls with prominent free rock faces, vertical crags and blocky angular scree debris. In contrast, only 4 lie on the Skiddaw Group rocks. Here the cirque forms are more subdued. More thinly bedded strata and intense cleavage results in the rock being more easily broken up and the debris produced being dominated by thin, small, platy fragments. Headwalls and sidewalls are still steep, but produce fewer bare, bold crags. The morainic and scree debris on the tarn edges are frequently well vegetated. Three of these tarns (Bowscale, Floutern and High Nook) are actually on altered Skiddaw Group rocks – material that has been baked and hardened within the metamorphic aureoles close to intrusions. Elsewhere over the Skiddaw Group outcrop cirque basins are scarce.

Figure16. Angle Tarn (Bowfell), seen from the summit of Bowfell. This almost circular tarn occupies nearly all the floor of the cirque. It lies in a true rock basin of volcanic rocks. A classic cirque tarn with steeply sloping shores at the back and sidewalls and deep water across the middle of the tarn. Rock and scree extend down to the shores.

Table 1 presents some basic data on these 20 cirque tarns and the small maps in Figure 17 arrange these tarns in order of their shapes. In the following pages there are some further descriptions and illustrations of the cirque tarns.

26

Table 1.

Cirque Tarns (in order of circularity)	Geology	Aspect	Max. Depth (m)	Altitude (m)	Area (m)	
Angle Tarn (Bowfell)	BVG	NE	16	579	35131	D
Blind Tarn	BVG	ENE	6.5	562	4269	M
High Nook Tarn	(SG)	N	‹ 1	221	6349	M
Stickle Tarn	BVG	E	14	469	83311	?
Levers Water	BVG	SE	37	411	148349	D
Keppel Cove Tarn	BVG	SE	8	556	25500	M
Blea Water	BVG	ENE	63	480	175186	D
Bleaberry Tarn	EG	NE	5.8	495	10257	M
Scales Tarn	SG	E	8	594	13355	D
Red Tarn	BVG	NE	26	719	80971	D
Low Water, Coniston	BVG	NE	14	544	19430	D
Bowscale Tarn	(SG)	N	17	477	27449	M
Sprinkling Tarn	BVG	NW	9	598	23428	?
Scoat Tarn	BVG	SW	18	596	44802	D
Small Water	BVG	NE	14	452	41967	D
Easedale Tarn	BVG	E	22.5	281	106394	?
Codale Tarn	BVG	ESE	7	465	13347	?
Goats Water	BVG	S	13	502	29337	?
Grisedale Tarn	BVG	NE	33	539	115900	D
Floutern Tarn	(SG)	E	3.5	375	13117	?

The Tarns are listed in order of their circularity – by measuring their Shape Index. This shows how close the shape of the tarn is to a perfect circle. It is calculated by the formula $1.27A/L^2$ where A is the area of the tarn and L is the maximum length across the tarn at the widest point. A perfect circle has an index of 1.0, The closer the figure to 1.0, the more circular the form. Angle Tarn with an index of 0.96 is the most circular. Floutern Tarn with an index of 0.17 is noticeable more linear. The tarn outlines and their index figures are shown in Figure 17.

Geology; BVG Borrowdale Volcanic Group
         EG Ennerdale Granite
         SG Skiddaw Group
       (SG) Altered Skiddaw Group

In the last column:
        M = Moraine dam to tarn.
        D = Definite rock basin
        ? = Possible rock basin, but could be partially moraine dammed.

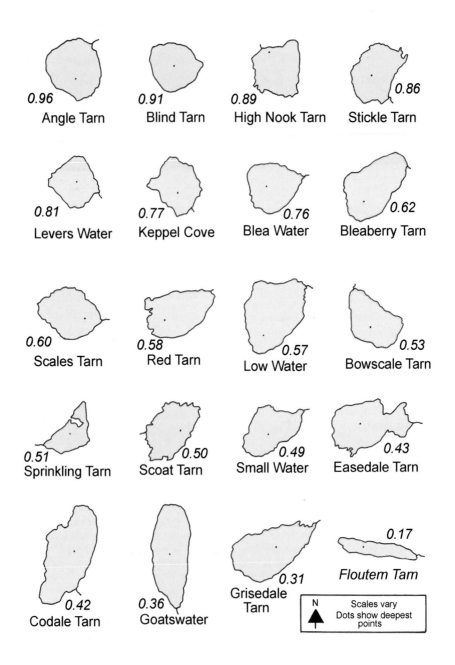

0.96
Angle Tarn

0.91
Blind Tarn

0.89
High Nook Tarn

0.86
Stickle Tarn

0.81
Levers Water

0.77
Keppel Cove

0.76
Blea Water

0.62
Bleaberry Tarn

0.60
Scales Tarn

0.58
Red Tarn

0.57
Low Water

0.53
Bowscale Tarn

0.51
Sprinkling Tarn

0.50
Scoat Tarn

0.49
Small Water

0.43
Easedale Tarn

0.42
Codale Tarn

0.36
Goatswater

0.31
Grisedale Tarn

0.17
Floutern Tarn

N

Scales vary
Dots show deepest points

Figure 17. Shape Indexes of the 20 cirque tarns.

Figure 18. Left: Blind Tarn, Coniston. (looking south). A small, almost circular tarn in a symmetrical basin with the deepest water at over 6m near the centre. Enclosed by an arcuate ridge of moraine on its eastern side. It has neither outlet nor inlet streams and hence its name 'blind'. Perched in a small cirque recess on the NE side of Brown Pike.

Figure 19. Right: High Nook Tarn. In a poorly developed and open cirque. A very shallow tarn less than a metre deep, with several islands of vegetation. It has a boggy shoreline and there has been some reinforcement around its outlet (at left) to retain it. There is considerable moraine in the basin which undoubtedly retains it.

Figure 20 Left: Stickle Tarn. The tarn occupies a rocky shelf high above Great Langdale. The cirque is dominated by the sheer rocky backwall of Pavey Ark (right) but with sidewalls little more than buttresses. There are significant moraines around the outlet, enclosing a smaller tarn. The shoreline is particularly stony with a rocky island and large boulders close to the northern shore. The water level is about 2m higher than the natural level because of damming to provide power for the Elterwater gunpowder works.

Figure 21.
Left: Levers Water.
It lies in a complex cirque feature in the Coniston Fells. The second deepest cirque tarn with a bowl shaped basin plunging to 37m. An enclosed rock basin occupying almost all the cirque floor. Dammed to provide water for the nearby mines, it now stands a few metres above its natural level.

Figure 22.
Right: Keppel Cove Tarn.
The tarn was once 8m deep with an almost circular outline and was contained by a distinct arcuate moraine. All that remains today is a boggy tarn bed and the breached moraine following the disastrous interference with the tarn for the Greenside Lead mining operations.

Old shore line

Former tarn bed

Figure 23.
Left: Bleaberry Tarn. Seen from the summit of High Stile, with Crummock Water in the background.

An oval shaped tarn lying in a basin dammed by a conspicuous moraine. The tarn lies on the Ennerdale Granite, but the backwall and some of the southern slopes of the cirque are cut into volcanic rocks. The tarn is particularly deep on its southern side. The whole area is a rather complex cirque feature with several separate basins.

Figure 24. Left:
Scales Tarn.
The only cirque tarn cut into rocks of the Skiddaw Group which are unaffected by thermal metamorphism. It lies in a well proportioned cirque with steep, bare rocky sides. The tarn is quite symmetrical with its deepest point near the centre.

Figure 25. Centre:
Red Tarn (Helvellyn).
This is the highest of all the cirque tarns and the most frequently quoted example from Lakeland. It is contained within a magnificent cirque cut into the eastern flank of Helvellyn with the arête ridges of Swirral and Striding Edges confining the tarn to north and south. There is a broad moraine around its outlet end with some huge boulders and slabs of rock along its line. The tarn floor is quite flat. The outlet area and tarn levels have been modified to provide water for the Greenside lead mines. (See also Frontispiece page 6).

Figure 26. Left:
Low Water, Coniston.
A definite rock basin cut deep into volcanic rocks. An asymmetrical basin with steep sides along its southern shores and the deepest point close to the rather pointed southern end. The north western half of the basin shallows very gradually towards the outlet. A very rocky shoreline.

Figure 27.
Left: Bowscale Tarn
It lies on the thermally
metamorphosed
Skiddaw Group rocks
within the aureole of
the Skiddaw Granite.
A classic cirque
feature with the
deepest point of the
tarn tight on the base
of the backwall.
Dammed by a very
conspicuous moraine.

Figure 28.
Right:
Sprinkling
Tarn (view
from the
lower slopes
of The Band,
below Great
End, looking
northwards).

This is not a typical cirque tarn and should perhaps be regarded more as a ridge-top ice scour feature. The outline is very irregular with small bays and promontories. The southern part is a fairly simple basin dropping to 9m in depth, but the northern section is very rocky, shallow and irregular.

Figure 29. Above: Scoat Tarn. A tarn in a distinct rocky basin in a high valley-head cirque. The slightly elongated shape relates to the SW-NE strike direction of the volcanic rocks. The basin is deep along its south eastern side (left in view).

Figure 30. Above: Small Water, seen from the Nan Bield Pass looking north eastwards, with Haweswater in the far distance.
A tarn that is quite deep for its area, lying in a typical rocky cirque basin. The structures in the underlying volcanic rocks account for its slightly elongated shape and the steep side to the basin along its south east side. There is a considerable amount of moraine around the rather complex outlet area, but the depth of the basin confirms the tarn is contained in an ice excavated hollow. The small tarn in the moraines is just visible to the left hand side of the outlet.

Figure 31. Above: Easedale Tarn. A tarn with two distinct basins; a main deep basin at the western end and a smaller shallower basin near the outlet (seen here in the picture above). The steep sided moraines around the eastern shores are very prominent (to the right in the view) and clearly partially dam the tarn.

Figure 32. Above: Low winter light on the terminal moraines at the outlet end of Easedale Tarn. A small tarn, perched in a hollow in the moraines can be seen at the extreme left.

Figure 33. Left: Codale Tarn. A simple elongated basin, deepest near the middle. It occupies a shelf at the head of the glacial stairway of the Easedale Valley. This is far from a classic cirque feature. Its position at the valley head owes much to modification by ice streams overriding the whole area and it is not easy to decipher how much of the tarn is moraine dammed. The view is from the southern end. The outlet stream is midway along the shore on the right – just beyond the two people standing on the small hillock.

34

Figure 34. Right: Goats
Water. View from Goat's
Hawse looking due south.
This is a distinctly oval
shaped tarn with a regular
basin deepest in the middle.
It clearly lies in a rocky
basin excavated into the
volcanic rocks but the outlet
area is difficult to interpret.
The whole area around the
tarn at its southern end and
the tarn floor itself is strewn
with large boulder debris.
Unusually the tarn lies in a
southerly orientated cirque.
(See also p.84).

Figure 35. Left: Grisedale
Tarn. View is from the slopes
of Dollywaggon Pike looking
south. Fairfield is to the left
and the slopes of Seat
Sandal to the right. The tarn
drains north eastwards (to
left). This is an impressive
rock basin of considerable
depth. Its oval shape is fairly
typical for a cirque tarn, but
unusually the deepest water
is towards the outlet end. Its
position is somewhat unusual
at the head of Grisedale and
it is noticeably lacking a
significant backwall.

Figure 36. Right:
Floutern Tarn.
(view looking east
towards the outlet
end)
This extremely
elongated tarn is
in a basin which
is difficult to
evaluate in terms
of the extent of
morainic damming.
Moraines and
boulder debris
enclose the full
length of the
northern shore of
the tarn (left in
view) and much

of the area around the outlet. The shoreline is mostly of boulders and low peaty
banks. The tarn itself is on the thermally metamorphosed Skiddaw Group rocks, but
the steep slopes of Great Bourne which form the backwall to this very open cirque
are made of Ennerdale Granite

There are in fact a number of small subsidiary tarns close to some of these cirque tarns, very much associated with the processes of glacial erosion that created these basins. In particular, in the morainic areas that surround some of them, the rapid downmelting of the ice and the rather haphazard way debris was dumped by the decaying glaciers left some areas of exceptionally irregular topography. In the huge, steep, moraines that dam the outlet area of Easedale Tarn for example, there are small peaty pools in some of the deep hollows (Figure 32). Within the huge moraine complex on the NW side of the outlet of Small Water there is a significant tarn contained in a depression some 30m long and around 8m wide (Figure 30). A few metres above the SW side of High Nook Tarn there is also a secondary tarn within the moraine debris. Again, close to the outlet of Grisedale Tarn on the north side, there is a small pool in a rocky ice shorn hollow. There is also a tarn in the terminal moraine of Red Tarn (Helvellyn) but it may be artificial.

Many other cirque basins across Lakeland did at some time in the past contain tarns, but have been progressively infilled by the accumulation of sediment washed in by streams from the surrounding slopes, and the gentle build up of peat and wetland vegetation. In the 13,000 years or so since the ice disappeared from the fells these natural processes have progressively, one by one, reduced the number of cirque tarns in the landscape. Beds of infilled tarns are a common sight. Good examples are in Gillercombe (Borrowdale), in several of the small basins adjacent to Bleaberry Tarn, at Blind Tarn Moss in Easedale or at Dry Cove Moss below Weatherlam in the Coniston Fells. The shallowest of the present day tarns, like High Nook, will be the next in line to infill.

Figure 37. Right: The infilled cirque basin of Blind Tarn Moss on the SE side of the Easedale valley, above Grasmere.

36

4. AREAL SCOURING BY ICE SHEETS

There are around 800 small lakes, tarns and pools in the Lakeland landscape that were created by extensive areal scouring of the bedrock surfaces by mobile ice sheets. Many of these features are unnamed, small and little more than rock pools. Together, however, they represent a very significant part of the story of how ice modified the upland areas. Amongst them are some quite large features, notably Angle Tarn (Patterdale), Burn-moor Tarn, Devoke Water, Blelham Tarn and Skeggles Water, but they need to be seen collectively as a group, along with the myriad of smaller features (too numerous to describe and illustrate in detail) to convey how ice action areally transformed the details of this landscape.

At the height of the Last Glacial Maximum (approx 21-26 ka) ice, at times up to 800m thick, covered all of the high ground of Lakeland. Thick, linear glacier streams filled the major valley routes and were gouging out the 'big lakes'. Cirque glaciers, high in the fells were excavating their basins. Collectively however, the district was under an ice dome feature with ice sheets moving radially outwards from the centre, overtopping ridges, riding over hilltops, cutting across everything in its path, areally scouring the surface. It produced tracts of glacially scoured bedrock, ice shorn crags, rocky knolls, *roches moutonnées* and irregular scoured rocky basins in which pools and tarns could later be contained. In NW Scotland such terrain is often described as *'knock and lochan'* topography from the Gaelic *cnoc* meaning a knoll, and lochan a small lake. It is under these conditions that the details of the under-lying geology become important. The ice exploited the weaker structures like fault lines, joints and softer beds of rock, while more resistant materials were able to remain as *knocks* and upstanding lumps. The geological texture of the terrain was revealed by these scouring processes. Laterally extensive flows of mobile ice picked out and lay bare the structural skeleton of the landscape. This type of terrain is particularly concentrated over the volcanic rocks of central Lakeland, on the intrusive granites of the west and on the hard sedimentary strata of the higher ridges of South Lakeland. Figure 38 shows the principal areas of this type of terrain and indicates the approximate numbers of lakes, tarns and pools in each area (labelled A-N on the map).

Broadly speaking there are three main situations where we find these areally scoured features; (see Figure 4).

1. On exposed ridge tops that were completely overridden by ice. (eg at Angle Tarn (Patterdale), Innominate Tarn, Siney Tarn, Stony Tarn, Skeggles Water, Devoke Water).

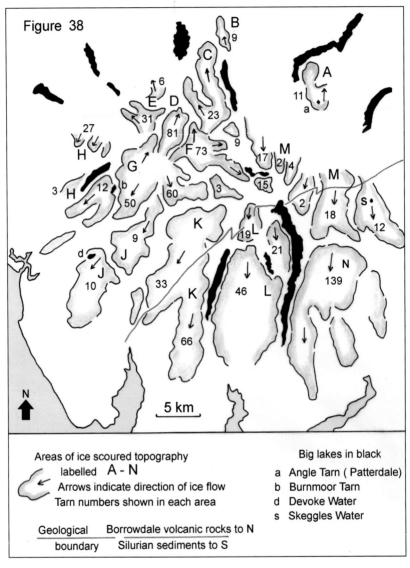

Figure 38

Areas of ice scoured topography
labelled **A - N**
Arrows indicate direction of ice flow
Tarn numbers shown in each area

Big lakes in black

a Angle Tarn (Patterdale)
b Burnmoor Tarn
d Devoke Water
s Skeggles Water

Geological   Borrowdale volcanic rocks to N
boundary   Silurian sediments to S

5 km

2. In ice scoured basin features where erosion was particularly concentrated due to the topographical situation (eg at Styhead Tarn, Dale Head Tarn, Harrop Tarn, Low Tarn (Wasdale) or Blackbeck Tarn).

3. Where scouring has been concentrated along weak structural lines in the underlying bedrock (faults, joints and strike features).(eg at Tarn at Leaves, Long Moss, Red Tarn (Wrynose), School Knott Tarn, Blelham Tarn, Snipeshow Tarn, Beacon Tarn).

There are many variations on these three situations. Local conditions and geology can usually explain individual features. In the following sections (labelled A-N as in Figure 38) some brief descriptions and illustrations of just the major examples of these features are presented. It would be tedious to list or even attempt to describe all of these 800 or so features. A walk across the Glaramara ridge, Seathwaite Fell or Tarn Crag in the central Lake District is more than sufficient to convince anyone of the futility of attempting an inventory or detailed account.

Area A. Angle Tarn (Patterdale) and the neighbouring ridge tops of Brock Crags, Angletarn Pikes and Place Fell.

Angle Tarn (Figure 39) is an excellent example of a large, ridge top ice scour feature. It is one of the most irregularly shaped tarns of the district, with two small rocky islets, several exposed rocks in the shallow waters, a low rocky peninsula extending into the tarn from the eastern shore, a rocky shoreline and all set in a landscape of ice shorn rocks. The floor of the tarn is equally irregular with numerous separate basins, all less than 9m deep. It has been excavated into a complex array of volcanic rocks bounded by a series of faults running broadly north to south, but with subsidiary faults between them. The outlet is over a rocky sill on the west side. On the ridge top to the north there is a small scour tarn on Stony Rigg and two minute tarns on Angletarn Pikes.

Figure 39. Above: Angle Tarn looking south towards Brock Crags. Outlet of tarn on the right. Rocky peninsula extending into tarn on left.

To the south, arrays of peaty pools (that almost defy counting) lie on the scoured summit of Brock Crags (Figure 40) and typify this type of terrain. Similarly the craggy ridge of Place Fell further north has seven small tarns amongst the rocky knolls and scoured bumps.

Figure 40. Left: Peaty pools on the summit of Brock Crags. Typical *knock and lochan terrain* – rough knock features to left, scoured hollow in foreground with peaty tarns. Illustrates the problem of tarn counting in such areas. Separate pool in far distance + three others in foreground. (Or should they all be counted as one?).

Area B. The long ridge of High Rigg – Low Rigg, lying between the Naddle valley and St John's-in-the-Vale.

This is a classic ice scoured feature. It has nine tarns along its crest, only one large enough to be named, as well as countless wet hollows and peat filled pools. Its shape is the result of its geological structure. It is made up of thick sheets of volcanic andesitic lavas and interbedded volcanic ashes, all dipping regularly at fairly low angles to the south. The stronger lavas stand out as prominent ridges and *knocks*, the less resistant ashes tending to form the hollows. The ice coming down the Thirlmere valley moved due northwards over this ridge, that is, in the opposite direction to the southwards dipping beds of rock (Situation 1. as shown in **Figure 41 below**).

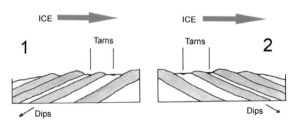

The net effect of this is seen in the detail of the ridge top. Ice moving northwards was sliding up over great tilted slabs of lava leaving them exposed as smoothed, ice moulded surfaces, whereas the exposed ends of the beds facing north, were plucked away by the ice to stand proud as rocky crags. Small tarn beds were excavated at the base of some of these north facing crags, or in north-south running linear depressions where ice broke through the ridges. Tewit Tarn, the largest and only named tarn on the ridge lies at the extreme northern end where the underlying geology is slightly more complex. It lies on the exposed top of a small exposure of the Threlkeld Microgranite (Figure 42).

Figure 42. Above: Top left and right, and bottom left – three unnamed tarns on the High Rigg crest. Bottom right – Tewit Tarn, with Blencathra behind.

Area C. The large interfluve between the Thirlmere Valley and Borrowdale. This was similarly overwhelmed with northward moving ice and was extensively scoured. Much of the ground is now covered with peat and some glacial debris and it is only in its western and south-western parts (Grange Fell and Great Crags areas) that tracts of classic *knock and lochan* terrain are found. It contains three interesting tarns – Snipeshow, Harrop and Dock – each with

41

distinctive features. The other 20 or so small pools are insignificant in themselves, but the Ullscarf area in the south is heaven for perfectionists devoted to tarn and pool counting. Choose a wet time of the year ! There are minute, dark, peaty pools and rocky hollows that constantly fill and dry up; far more than either the Ordnance Survey or even Wainwright recorded. You will need a GPS in this cheerless place.

Snipeshow Tarn on the north east flank of this area above the Naddle valley, is a real gem of a tarn. Little visited, it sits in a similar geological situation to the tarns on neighbouring High Rigg-Low Rigg. Dark beds of andesitic lava and volcanic tuffs dip southwards and have been smoothed and polished by the northward moving ice. On the north east side of the tarn there are superb, exposed striated slabs of rock scattered with perched boulders. The tarn has been etched out by ice working along the weak line of a NW-SE running tear fault in the rocks. The tarn

basin is very shallow, there is no obvious outlet stream, but water clearly seeps away northwards. A very large boulder dominates the eastern shore.

Figure 43 Right: Snipeshow Tarn, looking north. Prominent boulder on E. shore in centre of view.

Harrop Tarn (**Figure 44. left**) is a good example of an areally scoured basin feature. Standing on the shoulder of the fells above the Thirlmere Valley it lies in a very irregular ice scoured area. The tarn is now less than 5m deep and is clearly infilling quite quickly. It occupies only a fraction of the hollow in which it rests and its edges are difficult to define as the wetland vegetation builds out into the shallow fringes of the tarn.

Dock Tarn relates to a weak north-south line in the volcanic rocks which northward moving ice was able to exploit on the crest of Watendlath Fell. This is a very ice roughened area of crags and hollows. The tarn is very shallow, mostly under a metre in depth, with one rocky island and numerous protruding rocks at its northern end. It is progressively infilling at its southern end.

Figure 45.
Right: The
southern end
of Dock Tarn.

Probably the finest examples of tarn basins produced by areal scouring in the whole of Lakeland are to be found in **Areas D, E and F** and the northern part of **G** (Figure 38). All of these ridge tops are underlain by volcanic rocks where powerful ice streams moving northwards away from the highest ground of the central mountain core of the district were able to rough up the terrain and scour many small basins. There are for example 81 small tarns on the main Glaramara ridge (Area **D**), a further 25 on Seathwaite Fell (Area **G**) and over 20 on Brandreth – Hay Stacks and High Scawdel (Area **E**). (Figure 38).

Area D. On the Glaramara and Seathwaite Fell ridges the geological structures are the same as was illustrated on High Rigg-Low Rigg (Situation 1 in Figure 41) – the ice was moving northwards, but the predominate dip of the rocks is in the opposite direction (to the south). In places on the Glaramara ridge the dips in the volcanic rocks are quite steep; 50-60° at the northern end on Rosthwaite Fell and around 30° close to Lincomb Tarn. This leads to a very bumpy, irregular ridge top. The ice also scoured out the west-east strike of the rocks, resulting in many of the small tarns lying in deep west-east hollows (for example those around Lincomb Tarn and in the High House Tarn group).The largest tarn on the ridge, Tarn at Leaves, lies along a fault structure that cuts obliquely NW-SE through the ridge. (Figure 46)

Similar terrain is found across the top of Seathwaite Fell (Area **G**) (Figure 47). Styehead Tarn, on the western flank of the fell is a rather puzzling feature, but it is perhaps best seen as a type of scoured basin, albeit rather assymetrical in form. Ice scoured rocks rise up steeply along its eastern side, whereas the much lower western side is aligned with a fault in the rocks which its outlet stream, Styehead Gill cuts deeply into as it descends into the Borrowdale

43

valley. The tarn has shallow water along its western and southern margins where there has been considerable infill of stream deposits. In fact, a large fan of coarse debris from Aaron Slack, the very prominent gully on the west between Great and Green Gable, has built across the outlet end and may well largely dam the tarn. It is clearly not a cirque tarn as it lacks a headwall and any real sidewalls. It is 8.5m deep towards its northern end. (Figure 47).

Figure 46. The summit of the Glaramara Ridge

Top: view N. across ridge top from Allen Crags.

Middle left: High House Tarn group

Middle right: Typical small scoured basins.

Bottom right: Tarn at Leaves. View looking north

Figure 47. Left: The ridge top of Seathwaite Fell looking north, seen from Great End. Sprinkling Tarn in the shade in the foreground. Ice was moving northwards over this spur. Borrowdale Volcanic rocks dip southwards. 25 small tarn basins are scattered over the rough terrain of this area. The Borrowdale valley in the distance.

Figure 47. Above: Styehead Tarn seen from the slopes of Great Gable.
View looking eastwards with the scoured slopes of Seathwaite Fell above the tarn.
The tarn outflow down into Styehead Gill is to the left with the fan of debris from Aaron Slack building out into the tarn.
Note infill at head of tarn.

45

Area E. There are three small tarns on the summit of Brandreth, and six on the neighbouring top of Grey Knotts. All are small, unnamed, shallow and scattered amongst the rocky outcrops. To the west the even more irregular tops of the Hay Stacks area is another classic stretch of areally scoured ground. The two largest, named features, Blackbeck and Innominate (Loaf) Tarns are somehow just part of this great mosaic of water, rock and secretive depressions. Again this is a challenging area to count the tarn features – my own inventory comes to 22. Blackbeck Tarn is the largest and the most distinctive feature. It is pear shaped, quite shallow at its upper end and lies in a structurally aligned NNW-SSE running hollow. Its outlet tumbles down a steep rocky ravine into Warnscale Bottom at the head of Buttermere. It is shallow, reaching only 2.4m at its deepest point. Innominate or Loaf Tarn, as it was originally called, is even shallower and much more irregular. Nowhere does it reach a metre in depth and it contains four rocky islets and is floored with peat. It is a classic acid, nutrient poor, upland tarn. Many people regard the very small summit tarn on the extreme top of Hay Stacks as the real jewel in the crown of this ridge. Used as photographic foreground from this dramatic viewpoint it is has few rivals, even in Lakeland. It is small, ringed by rock and is distinctly orientated SW-NE with the structures in the heavily flow-folded lavas that form the summit.

Figure 48. The
Haystacks ridge.

Opposite page:
Innominate (Loaf)
Tarn and scoured
topography.
View looking east
with the Gables in
the background.

Top right:
Blackbeck Tarn

Bottom right:
The Haystacks
summit tarn.

To the north, the ridge top of Fleetwith Pike has three insignificant minute tarns on its scoured crest. Further north, across the Honister Pass, the shelf area of High Scawdel was also scoured by an ice stream, here cutting across the watershed as a diffluent flow rounding the brow of Dalehead to go over into the head of the Newlands Valley. It left in its wake, Launchy Tarn sitting on the crest of the ridge. It is little more than a very shallow rocky hollow, with two possible outlets where water seeps away, but alongside it are four other separate pools and numerous sub-pools, again so typical of this type of terrain. Overlooking the head of the Newlands is the much more interesting Dalehead Tarn (Figure 49). This lies in a rock basin. It has prominent crags along its eastern and north eastern sides and was clearly once much larger. There is an extensive area of infill on the south west side and it is a really delightful tarn for those interested in the variety of wetland plants that fringe its shores and gradually encroach into its shallow waters.

Figure 49. above: Dalehead Tarn seen from the slopes of Dalehead, looking SE across to the scoured High Scawdell ridge where Launchy Tarn is found. The tarn outlet is to the left and the infilled areas around the head of the tarn to the right.

Area F to the east has further extensive stretches of ice scoured ground scattered with small pools and tarns. On the Steel Fell ridge there are 9 small tarns. Similarly over the high tops north of Great Langdale, tarns dot the Rossett Pike ridge, Martcrag Moor and Thunacar Knott and there is a very fine stretch of *knock and lochan* terrain over Sergeant Man and Tarn Crags. The long ridge of Blea Rigg, Lang How, Silver How, between Easedale and Great Langdale is an intricate mosaic of small tarns, pools and rocky knolls. Even further east the isolated mass of Loughrigg Fell has a very confusing rocky summit containing 11 distinct tarns and numerous wet hollows.

Figure 50. Left: The heavily ice scoured summit ridge of Tarn Crag, scattered with small tarn pools, seen from the slopes of Sergeant Man looking east.

Figure 51. Right: Tarn on Lang How above the Langdale valley

Figure 52. Left: Youdell Tarns on Blea Rigg, above the Langdale valley. Langdale Pikes at left.

Area G contains some of the highest ground of the central volcanic fells – the Scafell area, Esk Pike, Bowfell and Crinkle Crags. Thick, mobile ice moved south and south-east off these fells, moulding and scouring the high ridge tops. 50 small tarns lie on the southern flank of this area on Eskdale Fell – Great How, and a further 60 over the rough ridge tops of the south easterly running spurs from Esk Pike, Hardknott, Crinkle Crags, Cold Pike and Pike of Blisco. In the extreme east, the summit of Lingmoor Fell is classic areally scoured terrain with the significant Lingmoor Tarn (Figure 53) and at least two other smaller tarns. Red Tarn (Wrynose) also lies in this section and is a particularly interesting tarn. It lies in a NNW-SSE running valley feature between Pike of Blisco and Cold Pike. The valley has clearly been scoured out by SSE moving ice but this may not have actually created a basin in which the tarn lies. Hummocky moraines left stranded on the valley floor by a small glacier at the very end of the glaciation (The Loch Lomond Stadial c. 12.2-11.9 ka) contain the tarn. It is a very shallow feature less than 2 metres deep. It drains northwards and both ends are rapidly infilling with stands of reeds. Within the moraines are two other very small tarns and numerous peaty pools. (Figure 54).

Figure 53. Left: Lingmoor Tarn. View northwards over the tarn with the Langdale Pikes in the distance, The tarn is on the ridge top amongst an irregular area of heather clad rocky slopes of volcanic rock. Numerous islands of vegetation and patches of reeds stretch across the shallow tarn.

49

Figure 54.
Left:
Red Tarn
(Wrynose).
View looking
NE towards
Great Knott
with Crinkle
Crags beyond.
The tarn drains
north into
Oxendale (to
the right in the
view).

At the southern end of area G, on Eskdale Fell, Stony Tarn and Eel Tarn are significant features. The former, as its name suggests is in a particularly rugged, rocky piece of topography. The tarn basin is cut deeply into basaltic volcanic rocks, but it is almost completely surrounded by the rugged tor-like terrain of the Eskdale Granite. A little way away, Eel Tarn is similarly perched amongst the bare granite outcrops. It is in a very open basin, filled with wetland vegetation. The shallow tarn, less than 2 metres deep is rapidly being encroached by reeds, sedges, bog bean and other marginal plants).

Figure 55. Above left: Stony Tarn – view from the head of the tarn looking SW.
Above right: Eel Tarn – view of lower end of the tarn, looking SW.

Burnmoor Tarn stands between areas G and H (Figure 56) and is a very large tarn that can also be included with these areally scoured features. It lies in an open col that runs through from Wasdale to Eskdale. This was a route that ice found easy to exploit and deepen. The basin is cut into a rather complex faulted group of both volcanic rocks and Eskdale granite, but the whole structural grain in the area aligns with the col feature. The tarn is 13m deep, but the northern end is shallow. The outlet stream is slightly unusual in that it emerges from near the northern end and then suddenly turns due south to run along the structures in the granite down into Eskdale,

Figure 56. Burnmoor Tarn from the slopes of Illgill Head. View looking east towards Great How. The ice was moving left to right. The outlet stream on the far side, emerges from the left hand corner of tarn and then turns right to flow southwards into Eskdale

Area H. The trio of Blea Tarn (Eskdale), Siney Tarn and Blind Tarn (Eskdale) lie south of Burnmoor on the spur between Eskdale and Mitredale. This again is scoured granite topography. The largest, Blea Tarn, sits in a rocky basin, surrounded by bold granite crags and is aligned with the joint patterns in the rock. It is around 5m deep with very clear water and rocky shores. In contrast Siney and Blind Tarns are extremely shallow, irregular pools choked with vegetation and surrounded by peaty ground. Both are less than a metre in depth but they are nevertheless remnants of scouring over this hilltop.

Figure 57. Above: left: Blea Tarn.   right: Siney Tarn.

51

The section of area H north of Wastwater displays further good examples of areally scoured rock surfaces dotted with small tarns. There are five very small pools on the spur running south from Haycock, two more near the head of Nether Beck, five on the summit of Middle Fell and three on Yewbarrow. The dominant feature, however, is Low Tarn, which lies in an area of severely ice roughened ground on the volcanic rocks of High Fell. It has an elongated, slightly irregular basin, but it is basically aligned with SW-NE strike direction of the rocks. It is relatively shallow (<3m) but typical of these features it has several irregular basins in its floor and numerous rocky bumps and boulders in the shallow waters around its margins. Over the surrounding fell tops there are eleven other small tarns and pools.

Figure 58. Left: Low Tarn: the outlet stream is at the left and the peak of Red Pike behind.

Around Nether Wasdale where the Wasdale glacier was becoming less confined by the steep fellsides either side of Wast Water, there is a fine stretch of ice scoured ground over the valley floor. The area is underlain by fine grained granite, part of the Ennerdale intrusion. Whaleback like lumps of granite, heavily smoothed and sculptured by the ice extend over the lakeside area (NY 1150054) and over High Birkhow (NY143045). Draped over the rock, particularly in the hollows, the ice has left a patches of glacial till which are picked out in the landscape as relatively rich green pasture land. Three significant tarns lie here in hollows in this till cover. Tosh Tarn has a very small catchment and lies amongst enclosed fields and is fringed with trees. It is less than 3m deep. Similarly, Woodhow Tarn is in a shallow hollow in the till. A small granite crag overlooks the northern end. Again it is shallow (around 2m), with sedges building into its northern end and edges of alder carr in places. The smallest of these tarns, Flass Tarn, on the south side of the valley has clearly suffered alteration and its original form is unclear, but it's setting in the till cover on the scoured valley floor is the same.

Figure 59.

Left: Tosh Tarn.
View looking south
over the till
covered floor of
Lower Wasdale.

Below left:
Woodhow Tarn.

Below right:
Flass Tarn.

Area J. This extensive stretch of fell country from Hardknott in the north across Birker Fell, Harter Fell, and Ulpha Fell down to the Waberthwaite Fells in the south, has few significant tarns, but small pools, old tarn beds and extensive peat filled hollows are common. Ice was able to move with ease over these hilltops. The northern section over the volcanic rocks is particularly rocky and irregular; the southern section over the Eskdale Granite is bolder, more rolling terrain. Only three tarns are large enough to be named. Low Birker Tarn on the volcanic rocks just above the Eskdale valley lies in a hollow amongst a complex wilderness of crags, rock outcrops, odd mounds of glacial till, swathes of bracken, heather clad slopes and peaty depressions. It is a shallow feature with wetland fringes and peaty banks with old tree stumps. It seeps away northwards.

Figure 60. Right:
Low Birker Tarn.
The view is looking towards
the outlet end.

53

Holehouse Tarn on the top of the Waberthwaite Fells is smaller, but in a very open hilltop position. It was clearly much larger at one time. There is little rock to be seen in its immediate surroundings, except for a small crag on its southern edge and numerous scattered boulders in the shallow water. Dense tussocks of Purple Moor-Grass *(Molinia caerulea)* and peat fringe the tarn, the peat in places showing signs of erosion. Devoke Water, however, is a very large tarn in this area; in fact with a surface area of 348,169 m^2, it is the largest of all the tarns to be covered in this book. Sitting in an open, shallow col on Birker Fell it represents a major ridge top scoured basin. It has a distinct 'upland' feel to it. Its shores are wet and stony. There are stretches of wetland around its margins and the surrounding fells of rough grassland, heather, cotton grass and craggy outcrops make this feel quite a bleak place. It lies in a huge rock basin scoured out by south-westerly flowing ice. There is a low ridge of glacial till partly around its outlet area at its western end, but this does not really form a significant containing feature. The outlet stream plunges steeply down a rocky ravine. There is some glacial debris plastered over the slopes at the head of the tarn. Hill Beck which feeds into the south eastern corner is building a conspicuous delta. The ground on the northern side of the tarn is formed mostly of Eskdale Granite; to the south the underlying bedrock is quite steeply dipping volcanic rocks. The actual line of the col feature and of the slightly elongated basin of the tarn itself are aligned with the junction between these two groups of rock. A prominent island of volcanic rock, with a lush tuft of vegetation growing on it, stands close to the southern shore. The water reaches 16m deep at a point close to the middle of the rather straight northern shore. Large areas of the outlet end at the west are shallow.

Figure 61. Left: Devoke Water from the head of the Water looking SW. The boathouse at extreme left stands close to delta being built out from the southern shore by Hill Beck. The rocky island close to southern shore is seen as a dark feature just right of centre. The outlet is at the lowest point on the far skyline.

Area K. This large area stretching from the Coniston Fells in the north down the spine of the Furness Peninsula to the south, contains some interesting tarns. The highest ground of the volcanic Coniston Fells has all the classic features of an upland glaciated area. Seathwaite Tarn and the major cirque basins have already been described. A few minor ridge top, scoured tarns can also been found, notably over Weatherlam and the Yewdale Fells. Ice generated over this high terrain spread south and south westward as a mobile sheet across the Dunnerdale Fells. This is some of the roughest, rockiest and distinctly nobbly ground to be found anywhere in Lakeland, particularly in the area of Caw, Stickle Pike, Tarn Hill and Great Stickle. This is an amazing wilderness of rocky knolls and crags of volcanic rock, peat filled hollows, old tarn beds and several small tarns and pools. The only named feature is Stickle Tarn. Here ice was moving southwards and was able to etch out a linear depression in the steeply dipping volcanic rocks. The tarn is now rapidly filling in. Dense stands of horsetails, pondweeds and bogbean stretch almost right across the shallow waters.

Figure 62. Above. Two unnamed tarns on Tarn Hill (SD210920) in the Dunnerdale Fells.
Left: typical morass of water, peat and clumps of vegetation in scoured hollow.
Right: Small rocky pool on ledge at upper left, infilled old tarn bed in foreground right.

Figure 63. Stickle Tarn, looking S towards outlet end.

There is a very sharp and important geological boundary running SW-NE across area K. The volcanic rocks of the Coniston and Dunnerdale Fells abut against the very different Silurian sedimentary strata to the south. The line is marked by an abrupt break of slope, the sediments to the south forming much lower ground, most of it below 250m. This boundary had a profound effect on the areal scouring by the ice and is fundamental in explaining the position and details of many of the small tarns on this lower ground. This same boundary line extends north eastwards to repeat the same situation in areas L, M and N, as we will see shortly. The boundary line is marked in red on Figure 38. Ice could move with relative ease over this Silurian ground and pass southwards down into Morecambe Bay. Generally, the beds of rock dip southwards or south eastwards. This is the opposite arrangement we met with over parts of northern Lakeland (area B, C, and D) (Situation 2 on Figure 41). Here in the south the ice was moving in the same direction as the rocks are dipping. These sedimentary rocks are mostly dark grey or black siltstones, mudstone and sandstones with occasional limestones. Geologists identify no less than 19 different Formations. Some strata are slightly more resistant than others, some stand out as craggy ridges, others were exploited by the ice and lie as lower vales. The geological map shows a series of bands of rock running across the landscape, broadly west-east, but at the western end more SW-NE. Ice scouring this terrain picked out the weaknesses, the position and shape of many of the individual tarns reflecting the underlying structures. (Figure 64).

Over the southern part of area K, particularly around Torver, the Silurian rocks dip SE whereas the ice was moving S or slightly SW, that is obliquely across the outcrops (Figure 64 - 2). There was thus a tendency for the ice to slide SW with the grain of the rocks and hollow out the strike vales. This created either long, narrow tarn basins as at Long Moss, or chains of small basins along the vales, as on Torver Low Commons. Also in this area there are N-S running faults in the rock that slice through and offset the outcrops (Figure 64 -3). Ice again picked out these weak lines scouring out basins that now contain tarns. The best examples are Beacon Tarn and Torver Tarn (Figure 67). Moving southwards to Blawith Knott, Heathwaite Fell and Kirkby Moor the topography becomes a little more irregular largely because the underlying bedrock is folded into slightly more complex structures. It is still heavily scoured ground with numerous small, shallow tarns in peaty basins. Lang Tarn and Burney Tarn are named features (Figure 68). The summit areas of Lowick Common similarly hold scoured tarns with Leech Tarn, Roerigg Tarn, another Beacon Tarn and several other small pools.

Figure 64.

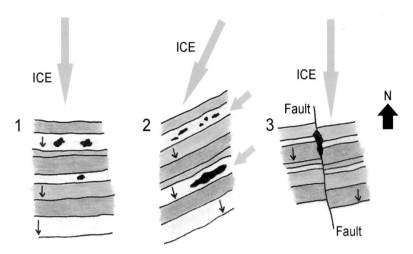

Outcrops of southerly dipping beds of rock	Outcrops of SE dipping beds of rock	N -S fault in southerly dipping beds of rock
Strike E-W	Strike SW - NE	Southerly moving ice exploits weak line of fault
Ice moving southwards across outcrops	Ice moving SW oblique to outcrops	
Tarns created in less resistant beds	Ice exploits the strike and produces linear tarns in vales	Tarn basin excavated along fault

Skeggles Water
Crook area

Long Moss Tarn
Blelham Tarn
School Knott Tarn

Beacon Tarn
Torver Tarn

Figure 65. Left:
The long narrow basin of Long Moss Tarn. It is 240m long and only 35m at the widest point. The water is barely 1.5m deep and much of the basin is choked with vegetation. It has been cut into steeply dipping siltstones of the Moorhowe Formation.

Figure 66. Above: Two of the many unnamed tarns on Torver Low Commons.

Figure 67. Above and below: Two tarns etched out along approximately N-S running faults. Above, Beacon Tarn, looking north along the fault line towards the Coniston Fells. Below, Torver Tarn. View is looking south. This tarn has a dog-legged shape with one section aligned S-N with the fault (from head of tarn in foreground at right, towards dip in fells on skyline), the second with the SW-NE strike of the sandstones of the Yewbank Formation), the section of the tarn that bends right in the view.

Figure 68.

Left:
Lang Tarn,
one of the
smallest tarns
in Lakeland to
bear a name.

Left:
Burney Tarn,
one of the
many tarns
on the area
of Heathwaite
Fell.

Area L. This area, lying between Coniston Water and Windermere mirrors area K. The extreme northern part is on the volcanic rocks, whereas to the south are broadly southerly dipping Silurian sedimentary strata. All of these ridge tops were swept across by southerly flowing ice. This is the picturesque 'roly poly' terrain of Beatrix Potter. It is a mosaic of lumpy ridges, hollows and valleys, small craggy outcrops and mounds of glacial debris. Much of it is now thickly wooded, but it is settled with cottages and farms tucked away in a complex topography. Scattered amongst all this are small tarns and pools. Considerable numbers of them have been modified into small reservoirs, fishing ponds, amenity features, or wildlife and conservation ponds. It is also an area where it has been easy to simply create new ponds, often just to make the landscape even more picturesque. To decipher the exact history of every one of these would be a long and somewhat pointless task, beyond the scope of the present work. Nevertheless we have here another extensive tract of ice scoured ground with a classic array of tarns and pools.

The volcanic ground at the northern end has all the features of this terrain. Slew Tarn, close to Skelwith Fold, is hidden away in woodland and a caravan park. It is choked with wetland vegetation and surrounded with carr woodland but it appears to be a natural feature surrounded by rocky crags along its western and southern edges. Nearby on the Brathay Hall estate is an example of a recently created tarn in this irregular terrain. Mortimere, was built in very

recent years to establish a 'field studies' pond. It has a simple earth dam and now looks very much part of this landscape.

Figure 69. Right: Mortimere, the dam is at far end.

The best known tarn in this area is Tarn Hows, visited by thousands of visitors every year, managed by the National Trust and an iconic Lakeland site. Again it is largely an artificial creation. Three small irregular tarns were combined into the present feature by the building of a small dam in 1865 at the SW corner. It was all part of the designed landscape of the Monk Coniston Estate. Part of the same improvements was the creation of Yew Tree Tarn, which is totally artificial and of High Arnside Tarn, now an enlarged fishing lake. All of these tarns were however, only possible because of the nature of the natural topography. Wharton Tarn which is in the same area is a natural feature retained in a small rocky basin.

Figure 70. Above: High Arnside Tarn.
Typical modified tarn basin in this irregular scoured terrain. Left, small masonry dam linking exposed rock outcrops has raised original water level by almost 2m.
Right, view looking northwards up the strike vale in the volcanic rocks along which the tarn basin was excavated by ice.

Figure 71. Tarn Hows, with Wetherlam in the background.

South from Tarn Hows the boundary on to the Silurian sediments is crossed. In the Barngates and Drunken Duck areas there are several small irregular tarns, many much altered, as well as small natural pools and derelict ponds on old quarry sites where the underlying Brathay Flags have been exploited. Blelham Tarn however, is a large and important feature. It is now a National Nature Reserve and a much researched site by the Freshwater Biological Association. Its origin lies in the scouring out of a strike vale in the underlying fine siltstone rocks of the Wray Castle Formation, and its linear shape is typical of how the ice responded to the underlying structures. There is however, a considerable amount of glacial boulder clay in the floor of this vale and the tarn nestles in this material. The bedrock can be seen at the upper end and on the south side, but the eastern outlet end is dominated by basin mires and wetland on the boulder clays. The tarn is 14.5m deep and is steadily being infilled as several small deltas are building out from inflowing streams.

Figure 72. Blelham Tarn, seen from the summit of Latterbarrow, with a glimpse of Windermere at right.

Claife Heights, the large area of wooded hilltops to the south has over 20 tarns along its summit, some of considerable size and eleven actually shown with names on the Ordnance Survey maps. Most of them have dams retaining them and are now fishing ponds, water supplies, or sites used for ecological research. Again, it was the effects of glacial scouring that made all this possible. Within the extensive tracts of land managed by the Forestry Commission in Grizedale Forest there are 16 tarns and pools. Only two however are natural features; the twin peaty pools at Grizedale Tarn (Below Figure 73).

The largest feature of the area, Wood Moss Tarn has been artificially created, as have Juniper Tarn, High Man Tarn and Goosey Foot Tarn, all now looking permanent parts of the landscape. Over recent years other small tarns have been impounded in this area, largely to create wildlife habitats. On the SW side of the Grizedale forests is Arnsbarrow Tarn on the very rough fell tops of Arnsbarrow Hill. This small, quiet tarn, fringed with lilies and floating vegetation is uneventful but it is a classic example of a scoured feature in classic *knock and lochan* terrain.

Figure 74. A rather wintery view of Arnsbarrow Tarn in its shallow basin.

Southwards, the advantages of these irregular landscapes have been exploited by the construction of substantial water supply reservoirs at Green Hows (Upper and Lower) and by the creation of the High Dam Tarns. This latter project was constructed progressively in the mid-Nineteenth Century to provide power for the Low Stott Park bobbin mill. The large and quite picturesque higher tarn is interesting in the way its irregular shape and rocky peninsulas reflect the strong SW-NE lineations and fold structures in the underlying rocks of the Bannisdale Formation. The ice scouring was sensitive to the structural configuration. Even further south, the quite large Boretree Tarn again betrays the nature of the rocks on which it lies.

Figure 75. Boretree Tarn

Here the Bannisdale Formation siltstones, mudstones and sandstones are intensively folded and cleaved with all the textures in the rocks aligned SW-NE. The elongated shape of the tarn with its distinctly sharp pointed ends runs with SW-NE grain. Originally there were three smaller tarns here. Damming has raised the water level to produce a single, larger tarn, now 12m deep. Like many of these features the result is now a rather inaccessible tarn with rocky shores and unnatural shorelines.

Area M. Here a series of spurs run south off the SE fells between the valleys of Rydal Beck, Scandale Beck, Troutbeck, Kentmere and Long Sleddale. The higher parts are on volcanic rocks, but the lower spurs in the south east extend on to the Silurian sediments. Over 50 ice scoured tarn basins lie over these areas. Most on the higher spurs retain their natural character, but as in the previous areas just described, over the lower Silurian ground, many tarns have been altered and many artificial ones created. On the high ridge crest of the Rydal and Scandale Fells there are consistent numbers of small ponds and minute mountain pools. On Rydal Fell above Grasmere is Alcock Tarn, now slightly enlarged with a small dam, but together with the minute Dockey Tarn nearby, they are both good examples of the work of ice scouring ridges and creating roughened terrain in which small tarns could collect.

Figure 76. Right: Allcock Tarn. View looking southwards from the slopes of Stone Arthur. The nobbly summit of Loughrigg Fell is seen in the centre of the view (in sunlight).

In similar situations small pools can be found on the neighbouring spurs to the east – on the Heron Pike ridge, on High Pike-Low Pike, on Ill Bell and Rainsbarrow Crag above Kentmere and on the Kentmere Pike interfluve. None are of great significance. On the ridge top east of Long Sleddale, in the saddle between the craggy scoured summits of Tarn Crag and Grey Crag, is Greycrag Tarn. The open saddle is filled with peat, in places up to 2m thick with deeply eroded 'haggs'. The shallow tarn is no more than a series of pools in the surface of the peat. Ice created this saddle as it moved south into Long Sleddale.

Figure 77. Left:
The peaty basin of
Greycrag Tarn – small
pools seen in the
distance. The view is
looking NE with Tarn
Crag at left.

Figure 78.
Right:
Scandale Tarn.
Large mound of
moraine behind
the tarn. Looking
west.

Close to the head of Scandale Beck, high in the volcanic fells, almost on the watershed with the valleys that drain northwards towards the Ullswater valley, there is Scandale Tarn. This is not an ice scoured feature. It is contained within a series of very hummocky and rounded mounds of moraine left abandoned by melting ice. It dates from the very last phase of glacial activity in Lakeland – the Loch Lomond Stadial stage which was a short, sharp period of very cold conditions when small glaciers were able to rebuild on the high ground between 12.2 and 11.9 ka. It is clearly one of the youngest tarns of the district (similar to Red Tarn, Wrynose already described). It lies at a height of 560m. It is barely 2m deep, rapidly infilling and choked with sedges along its southern edge.

The ground in the SE portion of this area noticeably falls in altitude once the boundary on to the Silurian sediments is crossed. The most significant tarn is Skeggles Water – a large, relatively shallow tarn sitting in a low saddle at 310m over southerly dipping siltstones and sandstones (Moorhowe and Yewbank Formations). There is little rock to be seen close to the tarn, except for some low outcrops along the eastern shore. It is nevertheless a ridge top where ice was able to exploit certain outcrops. South from Skeggles Water the ridge rises up on to the slightly more resilient rocks of the Bannisdale Formation. This is a wet, badly drained basin. The water in the tarn reaches only 3m at most and the edges are fringed with waterlogged boggy ground.

Figure 79. Skeggles Water. Left: View looking south from Cocklaw Fell down into the saddle where Skeggles Water lies. The higher ground of Sleddale Forest on skyline.

Right: Skeggles Water from eastern end. Low rocky crag to left, wetland fringes to right in shallow water.

Most of the other small tarns on these spurs are of little importance. It has been an area where many reservoirs (Dubbs, Borrans for example) have been created and numerous ornamental tarns constructed in private grounds and estates (Holehird, Middlerigg, Galls and Latrigg). Kemp Tarn however, is worth noting. This is a superb small tarn on the crest of Reston Scar overlooking Staveley. It illustrates as well as any other small tarn in the district the effects of the underlying steeply dipping strata on the shape and configuration of these features. Slightly confusingly the slaty Bannisdale Formation rocks dip to the north here, as there are some fold structures in the strata. Close to the SE corner of the tarn, alongside the prominent wall, it is easy to see the rock dipping as distinct slabs at 50-60° to the N. The tarn has been excavated almost W-E with the strike of the beds. Similar steeply dipping rock is visible on the northern shore of the tarn. It is drained by a minute outlet stream from its northern side – the stream almost immediately turning sharply eastwards to conform to the strike of the rocks. The tarn is very shallow (<1m) with rushes and sedges at both its western and eastern ends.

Figure 80. Kemp Tarn, looking north

To the east, on the spur end of Potter Fell between Staveley and Garnett Bridge in Long Sleddale, there is a significant group of tarns. This is an irregular area of ice scoured ground, again on slaty Bannisdale Formation rocks, but there are also considerable spreads of glacial boulder clay material. The three largest tarns, Ghyll Pool, Potter Tarn and Gurnal Dubs are all reservoirs, the latter however was a natural feature of three very small pools. Further east there are 12 small tarns scattered amongst the mounds of glacial debris and occasional rocky outcrops. The glacial debris melted out of the ice as it decayed, leaving conspicuous hollows for tarns to collect. Three of them are named on the Ordnance Survey maps – High, Middle and Low Taggleshaw – all are shallow and almost infilled with vegetation. Slightly further east two similar tarns in deep bowl like hollows in the till (sometimes referred to as the Routen Beck tarns) have open water. Even smaller pools lie in the same area to the south.

Area N. This area in the extreme south east extending south from Windermere and down the eastern side of the lake towards Crook and the Winster valley contains a very high number of tarns and pools. Few however are of any significance and individual descriptions would add little to the overall story. A great many of the features have been altered by damming to create reservoirs, mill ponds, fish ponds or wildlife sites. Many are on private ground and hence inaccessible. Several have been beautified and now lie in hotel grounds, on golf courses, or at private homes. Tracing the history of many is difficult and the extent to which some are natural features is difficult to ascertain. The overall landscape however is part of the story and again reflects the work of ice in creating sites where tarns would be left behind once deglaciation occurred or where it was easy to impound artificial tarns. Most of the ground is relatively low lying (below 250m), but it is an intricate mixture of low rocky hills and ridges, gentle depressions and wet valley areas. Much of it is wooded, but it is also farmed and populated. It practically all lies on the slaty sediments of the Bannisdale Formation which are gently folded. There is a strong structural grain to the topography, the ridges and depressions running broadly west-east. Several rocky hilltops show bare ice scoured ground with scattered small tarns and pools – Undermillock Common, Cat Crag and the areas NW of Crook are the best examples. Many small tarns lie in hollows where ice has worked out the W-E strike of the rocks. School Knott Tarn, one of the largest natural features is an excellent example, a linear feature rather like Blelham or Long Moss Tarns.

Figure 81. Right: School Knott Tarn, seen from SW outlet end.

Bolton's Tarn is similarly aligned along the strike. The rather complex two linear basin shape of Ratherheath Tarn, together with the four or five other linear pools in the woodland area to the north of it, also strongly reflect the same underlying geology. In the fields to the south, recently created pools also confirm this geological W-E grain in the countryside.

Figure 82. Ratherheath Tarn. Looking from the eastern end down one of the linear stretches of this very wooded area. It is under 4m deep and is used as an angling tarn.

In the SW of this area N, to the east of the high ground of Gummers How (SD 390885), there are four quite large tarns and some smaller pools. This is an interesting and quite attractive area, but all the tarns prove to be artificial creations. They are Victorian or Edwardian features impounded by small dams to produce fishing ponds and amenity waters. Two of them, Sow How Tarn and Heights Tarn have boat houses. The surroundings have areas of planted woodlands with exotic conifers, larch plantations and rampant rhododendrons in places. Middle Tarn, Heights Tarn and Duck Tarn have extensive floating and submerged vegetation. Sow How Tarn is more open. All of them are shallow and fringed with marginal wetland areas. Duck Tarn has been abandoned. Minute pools exist on the open fell tops to the east.

Figure 83. Above: left: Sow How Tarn, middle: Heights Tarn, right: Duck Tarn.

Running south from this area the irregular scoured ground has again been utilised for reservoir construction. There are significant ones just below Gummers How, at Simpson Ground and at High Newton. Even further south the rough ridge tops above High Newton has some small ice scoured pools, notably Newton Tarn and Tom Tarn. Even further SW, on the slightly detached upland around Bigland there are further small pools on the scoured hilltops at Tottle Bank (SD 375820) and at Stribers Allotment (SD 355815). Here also is the quite large Bigland Tarn. This is in a scoured basin at 160m on the ridge top. There has been some modification around its shores, but it lies in a basin of sandstones of the Bannisdale Formation. A N-S fault in the rocks accounts for its position, and the line of the low col area, now plugged with glacial debris, at its northern end. Quite steep rocky slopes enclose the southern part of the tarn which seems to be largely fed by spring flow.

Figure 84. Bigland Tarn, the southern end.

Apart from all the areas of areally scoured ground just described in the previous sections, there are some other scattered patches of this type of terrain elsewhere in Lakeland. Overlooking Ennerdale on the northern side of the Haycock – Scoat Fell ridge there is the minute Tewit How Tarn sitting on a northerly pointing scoured spur. It was much larger at some stage. Open water now covers only about a quarter of the tarn at its outlet end. There are other minute features on the nearby Ennerdale high fell tops to the west. Similarly on some of the ridges running down to Ullswater in the NE, ice scouring has created small pools and tarns. Sheffield Pike, Birkhouse Moor and the Gowbarrow areas are examples. There are also a few named tarns on the ridge tops above Swindale and Haweswater. Haskew Tarn for example lies in the very irregular area of Swindale Common. The tarn itself lies on deep peat that has built up in an open rocky basin. It has peaty banks and extensive spreads of sedges and horsetails in the shallow waters. There are other pools on this ridge too. On the opposite side of Swindale the maps show Scalebarrow Tarn in similar terrain. If you go to find it however, it can only be located by subtle changes in the vegetation cover and a minute pool. On the northern side of Haweswater there are recordable pools on Bampton Commons and an intermittent tarn amongst the tangle of ice shorn crags near Four Stones Hill. Further NW is the minute Rough Hill Tarn. The most significant tarn is Little-water Tarn on the much lower ground close to the lower end of Haweswater. This is a secretive place, reminiscent of the land-scape around Tosh and Woodhow Tarns in Wasdale. It is in irregular ice roughened terrain with glacial drift filling the hollow in which this gentle, circular tarn nestles.

Figure 85. Upper: Haskew Tarn, Lower: Tarn bed below Four Stones Hill (NY 491163).

Overall, these descriptions of this large group of areally scoured small lakes and tarns in these ice roughened terrains has demonstrated how they form a very significant and distinctive part of the Lakeland landscape. It must be remembered however, that they are highly dependant on the underlying geology. This type of terrain was not produced by the ice over the large tracts of Skiddaw Group rocks in northern Lakeland.

5. SOME OTHER TARNS OF THE HIGH FELLS

There are a number of other small tarns and pools scattered across the highest parts of the Lakeland Fells that do not fall into any of the categories of tarns discussed so far. They are all small, clearly not cirque tarns and do not relate particularly to areal scouring by ice across exposed fell tops. They are, however, natural features that relate to the way ice and cold climate conditions in the last glacial phases left this landscape and to the surface processes active in the period since the ice disappeared.

TARNS ON ROCK LEDGES

There are a few small tarns that lie stranded on rock ledges high on the flanks of some of the higher parts of the central fells (Figure 4). Broadcrag Tarn, perched at 840m on the south facing crags of Scafell Pike is the best example. This is the highest tarn in Lakeland. It is no more than 12m long and rests in a tangle of blocks, boulders and crags on a rocky ledge of well jointed dacitic lavas. The water in it is less than 1m in depth with spongy spreads of sphagnum moss in the shallow waters on the NW and SW sides. Just by chance water has found a place to collect in this jumble of rocks. No particular glacial or weathering processes account for its position. It may not have been there for a particularly long time, current processes of rock fall, frost and slope degradation constantly change such sites. Its long term existence is clearly in doubt, even in very dry summers it loses its water. There is a second very small minor rock pool on the same slope about 50m nearer Mickledore.

Figure 86. Above: Broadcrag Tarn. Left: Tarn arrowed on S. slopes of Scafell Pike. Right: Tarn seen from western end.

In a somewhat similar situation on the western side of Scafell Pike at around 655m there is Lambfoot Dub. Again this is on a distinct rocky ledge. It is little more than 30m long, its shape apparently the reason for its name. Angular boulders of volcanic rock lie along its E and SW shores. Water seeps away at both ends.

Figure 87.

Left: Lambfoot Dub (centre of view) seen from Ill Crag looking north. Part of Styhead Tarn is visible in the distance.

On the whole of this western flank of the Scafell Pike area the volcanic rocks dip eastwards into the central area of the collapsed caldera structure of central Lakeland. Consequently there are many eastward tilting slabs which form natural sites on which water can collect, whereas the natural drainage is westwards. Nearby, there are many other small ledge ponds, notably Round How Tarn (NY220081) between Round How and Broad Stand. This was once a much longer stretch of water. Here the easterly dips in the rock are clear to see. There is a minute second pool on a dipping ledge of rock just a few metres along at the eastern end. A slight distance away to the SW there is a further ledge pool, not on most Ordnance Survey maps but the indefatigable Wainwright records it (Scafell Pike 8). Nearby, over the slabs of Criscliffe Knotts (NY227083) and Middleboot Knotts (NY214081), again we have strongly dipping slabs of rock with numerous rock pools lodged within them. This area was however heavily scoured by northerly moving ice and is really *knock and lochan* terrain.

Figure 88. Above. Two small unnamed ledge tarns on Middle Boot Knotts. View is looking N with Great Gable in distance.

Dry Tarn (NY216098) on the steep SE flank of Great Gable at 660m also falls into this group of ledge tarns. As its name suggests it is often without water. It is canoe shaped, about 35m long and 5m wide There are no obvious outlets.

71

TARNS ON ARETES

The narrow, often sharp, rocky ridges left between side by side cirques basins are know as arêtes. These irregular strips of terrain often hold small basins. They have minute catchment areas. Rough Crag, the long straight arête between the Blea Water cirque and Riggindale, above Haweswater, has a number of pools along it. The largest tarn at Caspell Gate (NY450113) is in a major dip in the ridge. It is shallow with no obvious outlet but seepage towards Blea Water seems to occur.

Figure 89. Above and left: Caspell Gate Tarn. Left is view looking E down the arête towards Rough Crag. Above is view of the shallow tarn with the crags of the Blea Water cirque behind and left.

TARNS ON SUMMITS

The very tops of the fells, which may be reasonably flat, also hold tarns. Perhaps surprisingly there are quite a number in these positions. Using the terminology of plant ecologists, summits should actually be *'shedding sites'* as opposed to *'receiving sites'*, - that is places that shed water, rather than receive (collect) it. Summits really have no area of catchment, so in reality, tarns that occur in such high spots must be largely fed by precipitation (not a problem over the Cumbrian fells).

On the flat NE end of the rocky summit of Red Screes (776m), above the Kirkstone Pass, there are in fact 4 small tarns. The largest one has rocky surrounds and always appears to hold water **(Figure 90 right)**. The smaller ones are peaty hollows. There are also pools right on the summit of Whin Rigg (535m) above the Wast Water Screes and on the flat summit of Robinson (737m). In both cases they are largely contained within thin peat and the surface regolith (the loose mantle of broken down rock and soil material that lies over the summit).

Figure 91.The summit of Robinson (NY202168). The almost featureless summit has two groups of small pools (left and right above). All are extremely shallow and dry up regularly. They contain thin peat and scatters of small rocky debris (Skiddaw Group).

TARNS IN SADDLES

A more distinctive site for small tarns in high locations is in saddles between summits or in broader open saddle features along major ridges (Figure 4). Saddles will tend to be *'receiving sites'* where water naturally gravitates down into a low feature. The summits of Blencathra, Illgill Head, and Black Combe illustrate this situation. In all three cases the actual summits have two very gentle rounded swellings forming the highest ground. Nestling in the slight depression between them lies a tarn. A careful look at the summit ring contouring on the Ordnance Survey 1:25,000 scale maps clearly illustrates this. Other similar examples occur on Lank Rigg, above Ennerdale, and on Stony Cove Pike and Caudale Moor, above Patterdale.

Figure 92. Above: The small summit tarn on Blencathra

Figure 93. Left: The summit tarn on Black Coombe, a small feature with numerous tussocks of vegetation in the shallow water.

73

Saddle features of larger proportions, where there are distinct drops in summit ridges between neighbouring summits, provide even more good examples. Classic examples are Kirkfell Tarns and Beckhead Tarns on the Kirk Fell – Great Gable ridge, the tarns at Dore Head between Yewbarrow and Red Pike (Wasdale), Carlside Tarn between Carlside and Skiddaw, Three Tarns between Bow Fell and Crinkle Crags and the group of tarns in the saddle between Whin Rigg and Illgill Head (Wasdale). Many saddles accumulate peat and there are examples of pools in these situations which are difficult to

categories and probably better placed with the peat tarns discussed in a later chapter. Interestingly this situation is found over several fells based on the Skiddaw Group rocks of northern Lakeland, an area, as we have seen, that did not respond to deep areal scouring by ice. The saddle of Flag Pots between Lonscale Fell and Little Man (Skiddaw), the minor saddles on the Knott Rigg – Ard Crags ridge and the northern spur of Hindscarth all have peat pools in this situation. Elsewhere Quagrigg Moss on Great How (Eskdale), the saddles between Branstree and Selside, above Haweswater, Black Brow on Little Hart Crag (Patterdale) and Minum Crag on Maiden Moor are other examples.

Figure 94.
Saddle tarns.

Above: The two tarns at Beck Head.

Riight: Kirk Fell Tarn. In these positions tarns are often elongated across the line of the saddle, because of wave action on the peat banks, due to strong winds blowing through the saddle.

Figure 95. Above left: the larger of the two tarns at Beck Head. Frequently dry as in the picture, but elongated along the line of the saddle. Above right: similar feature at Kirk Fell, long elongated tarn with low peat banks. Over 1m deep and about 70m long and 20m wide.

Figure 96. Above: Tarn in the saddle below Branstree., above Haweswater. Tall survey pillar in view at right of tarn.

Figure 97. Above: Tarns in the saddle below Whin Rigg, Wasdale. A group of shallow tarns, often dry with peaty floors as in picture to right.

LAKELAND'S MOST UNUSUAL TARN

In the floor of the Mosedale valley, close to the head of Wasdale, there is a most unusual and rare type of tarn feature (NY 183100). Unfortunately, depending on when you go, although it is alongside a major footpath, it is easily overlooked and now looks more like a wet peaty patch and does not always have much standing water in it. It has recently been identified by researchers as a possible 'avalanche tarn', or a snow avalanche impact pit. The whole feature is circular, about 50m across and has a curved rampart surrounding it. The centre is now largely infilled with peat, with two patches of open water, but clearly at some stage in the recent past it was an open tarn. It is the result of snow avalanching from the slopes of Kirk Fell down a noticeable gully to the east, on to the flat floor of Mosedale below. The circular rampart feature is the result of the valley floor sediments being thrown out into a ring by the avalanche impact. These features are rare in the British landscape and this is the only example in Lakeland. They are well documented in other mountainous areas of the world, with classic examples in Norway and particularly in the Fjordland region of South Island, New Zealand. They are particularly associated with steep mountain slopes where there is an abrupt change of slope with the valley floor. In this particular case the top of the gully is around 700m, the pit lies at 135m and the long slope from Kirk Fell approaches 30 degrees.

Figure 98. The Mosedale avalanche tarn bed.
Seen from the lower slopes of Kirk Fell.

6. NATURAL DAMS

The hand of man in building masonry, concrete or earth dams to pond back waters and create reservoirs is all too evident in many parts of Lakeland. There are, however some good examples of small lakes and tarns that have been impounded by natural landscape processes. Rockfalls, landslips or deposition of debris by glaciers or streams can all form natural dams.

OVERWATER

Overwater is a significant sheet of water, bigger than two of the 'Big Lakes' (Brothers Water or Elter Water) and fourth in order of size of these smaller lakes and tarns. It was slightly altered in the 1920's to provide a water supply for nearby Wigton, but comparing the outline of the lake today with the first edition 6 inch to one mile Ordnance Survey map produced in 1869 the shoreline is remarkably similar. A low grassy bank curves around the north-eastern end with a three stepped red sandstone masonry spillway at the stream exit. It is now 18m deep. It lies on the northern edge of the fell country in a shallow valley that runs north eastwards along the foot of the fells. Towering over it to the south and east are the Uldale Fells formed of mainly slaty Skiddaw Group rocks. The terrain to the west and north is much lower and more subdued where a complex array of volcanic rocks is heavily covered with glacial boulder clays. The lake has been naturally impounded by a huge fan of stream debris brought down into the valley by the combined forces of Dale Gill and the head streams of the River Ellen pouring fine, slaty debris from the Uldale Fells **(Figure 99 right)**. These slaty rocks have been intensively weathered and shattered by ice erosion and 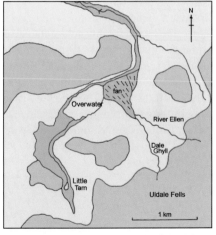 the valley heads in the area are choked with this material. The head of the River Ellen is today entrenched into deep spreads of loose rock debris particularly in the area of Crag Wood (NY267345) – all awaiting one day to be swept down towards Overwater. There are similarities here with the situation at Brothers Water where a side stream has built out fan debris into a main valley blocking the drainage. Nearby at Melbecks (2 kms south of Overwater) along a very similar stream (Millbeck), the very severe storms of January 7th. 2005 moved millions of tons of debris down from these Uldale Fells onto farmland causing extensive local damage. Overwater is a quiet locality. The edges of the lake are not very accessible, farmland stretching around most of its shores. At the upper end alder carr, reed beds and wetland areas surround the inlet stream.

Figure 100. Above: Overwater, seen from the north east.
The fan which dams the lake is picked out by the light green fields in the foreground in front of the lake. The River Ellen and Dale Ghyll enter from the left.

Upstream, lying in the same valley is Little Tarn (formerly known as Nevin Tarn). This is a tranquil spot, secluded and off the beaten track. The build up of the fan that contains Overwater also impeded the drainage higher up the valley system. The Ordnance Survey recorded the natural height of Overwater at 624.7 ft. and that of Little Water as 638.1 ft. – a difference of only 13.4ft. (4.08m). The two are around 1200m apart; the sluggish stream from Little Water running down a low gradient on the wet, boggy floor of the valley. Little Water is highly enriched, with continuous margins of zoned wetland vegetation. It is very shallow (3.5m) with a muddy, peaty floor and is fed by springs.

Figure 101.
Right: Little Water.
The view is from the western side of the tarn with the Uldale Fells in the background

GREENDALE TARN (Front cover)

Greendale Tarn has several unusual features. It lies in a straight, hanging valley on the northern side of Wasdale aligned along a north-south running fault line in the volcanic rocks. The tarn is close to the head of the valley which is an open col feature, only 60m higher than the surface of the tarn. A diffluent tongue of ice from Mosedale to the north clearly cut across this col into Greendale, seeking a southerly route. The fault is responsible for a distinct asymmetry across the valley. Along the eastern side, steep rugged crags on the slopes of Middle Fell drop right to the tarn edge, whereas gentle, concave, wet peaty ground on the west, gradually rises up to the swelling, ice scoured slopes of Seatallan. The tarn basin also has an asymmetrical cross profile with the deepest water extending down to 9m along the eastern shore, but very shallow stretches along the western side and towards the outlet at the southern end.

Figure 102. Above: Greendale Tarn seen from the outlet. The steep slopes of Middle Fell are to the right, the more gentle slopes of Seatallan to the left.

The tarn has been impounded in this shallow basin by extensive spreads of coarse rocky debris that has fallen from the crags and been moved down the slopes of Middle Fell on the eastern side of the valley. The outlet area of the tarn is formed entirely of bouldery debris, with no sign of bedrock for almost 1km. downstream of the outlet and no evidence of morainic debris. There are many substantial boulders standing in the shallow water at the southern end of the tarn and some huge detached blocks (>5m) littering the low ground near the outlet. Most of this debris is sub-angular, lichen covered and lies as extensive spreads of bare openwork boulders over the hillslopes.

Figure 103: Left: The debris strewn slopes of Middle Fell in the area below the outlet area of Greendale tarn.

HARD TARN

This is a little gem of a tarn on a rocky ledge at 690m on the side of Nethermost Crag in the Helvellyn Fells.

Essentially it has been created by a rockfall of debris on to a rock ledge impounding a small tarn that is little more than a pool. Its clear waters are less than a metre deep with many of its margins far less than that. It is about 40m across and has a shape strikingly similar to the outline of Australia. Its features and its formation are entirely due to the circumstances of its geology. The tarn nestles on a thick slab of dark, greenish volcanic tuff. The fact that the slab tilts gently into the hillside at about 6° helps to explain why water collects here. The slab is crossed by two sets of joints in the rock, some of which

Figure 104. Above: Hard Tarn, seen from Nethermost Crag. The tarn is on the ledge, slightly to the right of centre in the view.

have quartz veins along them. The dominant set of these joints run NW-SE across the rock slab and when the tarn is full, two trickles of water run along the lines of these joints to its SE edge and serve as outlets and maintain its height. Water also seeps away at the W end through a mass of scree debris. Steep vertical slabs of strongly jointed rock run around the northern rim. Along the NE side large boulders and rockfall debris from the crags above have crashed down on to the rocky slab and dam the tarn (Figure 105).

Figure 105. Above: Hard Tarn. View from above the tarn looking east.The steep valley head of Ruthwaite Cove is in the right of the view. Rockfall debris is seen at the top left. Water seeps away at the pointed outlet in the immediate foreground. The walker in the view is standing on the rocky slab over which water trickles when the tarn is full.

SAND TARN

Sand Tarn lies on the north-west side of the summit area of Wild Boar Fell in the extreme east of Lakeland. This is an area of the County formed of Carboniferous rocks - thick beds of flat lying sandstones, gritstones and shales forming a 'layer cake 'landscape (Figure 106). The flat topped moorland summits are scattered with many tarns in the peat (see later section). Along the flanks of the fells, however, landslipping is common - rocks of high strength like the sandstones and gritstones lie on shale beds which fail. Sand Tarn is a perfect example of a tarn created by landslipping in this situation. It has a slightly irregular oval shape nearly 150m long and no more than 60m wide. It lies on a shelf contained by landslip debris of big sandstone slabs along its outer western edge. It is shallow with several islands covered with tussocky vegetation. There is no obvious outlet but water seems to seep away at the SW corner. There is a sandy beach at the northern end which may reflect the prevailing south-westerly winds which

81

drift weathered material towards this end. It is on record the sand was exploited to be used to sharpen knives and scythes by making 'strickles' by sticking the coarse sand to wooden blocks with tar.

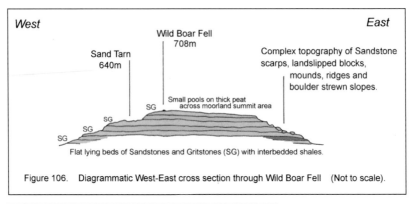

West   East
                                    Wild Boar Fell
                                        708m
                    Sand Tarn   Complex topography of Sandstone
                    640m   scarps, landslipped blocks,
                                                       mounds, ridges and
                                                       boulder strewn slopes.
                              Small pools on thick peat
                        SG   across moorland summit area
                    SG
                SG
            SG

    Flat lying beds of Sandstones and Gritstones (SG) with interbedded shales.

Figure 106.   Diagrammatic West-East cross section through Wild Boar Fell   (Not to scale).

Figure 107. Sand Tarn.

Left:
View from the slopes of Wild Boar Fell. The sandy beach is just seen at the right hand end of the tarn. There is a separate small, peaty pool to the right in the same depression.

Below:
View from the SE end.

The eastern flanks of Wild Boar Fell are a complex tangle of landslipped slopes. Slumped and slipped masses of debris now cover the ground as the slopes have been worked back by erosion and slope failure. Several hollows on these slopes also hold small tarns (Figure 106). The same situation is also found on Swarth Fell, the continuation of this same ridge to the south. Here again there are small landslip pools on its eastern flank (Figure 108).

Figure 108. Small pools in landslip topography. Above left: Unamed pool in the chaotic slipped terrain just N of Low White Scar (SD 761980). Above right: Pools at the base of Swarth Fell Crags (SD 757969).

THRELKELD KNOTTS

Where landslipping and slope failures occur, very irregular topography results, as we have just seen on Wild Boar Fell. What may be England's most massive rock slope failure is at Threlkeld Knotts, on the northern end of the Helvellyn ridge, below Clough Head (NY 328233). Here a chunk of the mountain side of about 1.2 km^2 has broken away from the steep face of Clough Head and now lies as an irregular and complex mass of rock known as Threlkeld Knotts. Within this displaced terrain of irregular ridges, sinuous depressions, bumps and hollows there are two small unnamed tarns (NY 329229 and NY 329228) and numerous wet basins. This whole feature, and hence these tarns, date from a time after the main glaciation of the district and are a direct result of the massive failure of the rocks on this hillside.

Figure 109. Left: The corrugated mass of Threlkeld Knotts seen from the summit of Clough Head. One of the small tarns is in the centre of the view.

83

GOATSWATER

As a footnote to this discussion of tarns created by natural damming processes, we must go back briefly to reconsider Goatswater. This has already been included as a cirque tarn, but it is a problematical site and it is possible that it too may be a tarn dammed by a natural rockfall. The available evidence is equivocal. As a cirque it has some unusual features. First it faces south, which is not an ideal orientation for cirque development. Secondly, in spite of its height (502m), there is evidence that this basin was not occupied by a glacier in the mini glacial phase known as the Loch Lomond Stadial at the very end of the glacial period when similar high cirques in Lakeland were reoccupied by ice. It is also very striking that it lacks a real headwall and that its highest enclosing crags lie along its sides - Dow Crag to the west and the side of the Old Man of Coniston to the east. The tarn lies in an undoubtedly ice modified valley head, but the waters could be impounded by scree debris at the outlet end. There are huge quantities of exposed blocks around the outlet area, many standing in the shallow water of the tarn and spreads of boulders are known to lie on the floor of the tarn. Sound bedrock in situ is only seen some 250m down valley of the outlet and at a level below the tarn floor. Eastern facing crags in the Coniston Fells (Dow Crag in this case), are seen to have shed large quantities of scree debris as result of frost action and slope instability after the glaciation.

Figure 110. Above: Goatswater seen from Goat's Hawes looking due south, with the screes of Dow Crag to the right and the slopes of the Old Man of Coniston on the left.

7. PEAT TARNS

Peat is essentially partly decayed plant material that accumulates in wet places where the annual input of dead organic matter from the vegetation cover exceeds the annual breakdown of the material. In Lakeland, peat accumulation has occurred in two quite different locations; on the 'mosses' of the Solway, West Cumbrian and Morecambe Bay lowlands, and over the 'blanket bogs' of the high fells and moorlands. Small lakes and tarns are features of both areas.

THE LOWLAND MOSSES

Cumbria has some of the finest examples of lowland mosses in the whole of Britain. When the landscape finally emerged from its cover of glacial ice (at around 14.7 ka) and the climate began to warm abruptly, there were extensive areas of the lowlands that held standing water in gentle depressions in the irregular spreads of glacial debris that the ice had left behind. Here were classic wetland sites, low lying, ill drained, many close to sea level, where peat bog formation found ideal conditions. The evolution of these areas is complex and today many of these areas are much changed through peat extraction and man-made drainage and land use alterations. Some stretches of open water still exist, but they are difficult to interpret and few remain in a natural state. It is difficult to determine whether open stretches of water have persisted since their inception, much more likely the remaining pools must represent depressions in the peat, or points where drainage modifications have led to water retention. Many of the pools marked on the Ordnance Survey maps are artificial creations relating to peat extraction. Scaleby Moss 8 kms NE of Carlisle still has several pools on its surface. It lies in a saucer of boulder clay but it has been greatly modified by peat extraction. 12kms west of Carlisle is Oulton Moss and the adjoining Martin Tarn. The moss has been partly cut for peat but still retains considerable depths in places. The tarn is a large oval feature, rather inaccessible and fringed with fen and woodland. It must sit in a basin in the boulder clay and is perhaps best regarded as a kettle hole feature (see later section) rather than a peat tarn. Elsewhere there are peat pools on mosses at Salta Moss just north of Allonby on the coast, and in the south, Roudsea Tarn and pools on Foulshaw and Meathop Mosses illustrate similar situations.

BLANKET BOGS

Tarns on the upland blanket bogs present some very interesting and puzzling problems. The classic location is the Pennine summit plateau of Dufton Fell, but similar plateau tops at Wild Boar Fell, Baugh Hill, Rise Fell (above Dent), Whernside and Barbon High Fell, all in the east, also contain tarns in the peat surfaces. In the Lakeland fells, smaller stretches of blanket bog exist over some of the more even and gentle summit areas, and again small tarns in peat can be found. Greycrag Tarn and Haskew Tarn have already been referred to, as has Quagrigg Moss (Eskdale). There are stretches of peat over some of the fell tops of the northern fells (based on Skiddaw Group rocks) where small peat pools exist - for example on the Uldale Fells, Knott and Great Calva. Another minute example is the tarn and a series of peaty pools on the extreme summit of the Calf, close to the highest point of the Howgill Fells (NY671974).

In the immediate post-glacial period (from about 11.5 ka) peat was not initially accumulating in these locations. A long period in relatively dry conditions first saw pioneering vegetation communities becoming established with herbs, shrubs and scrub gradually evolving into birch woodland. With climatic change to warmer and wetter conditions round about 7.8 ka (the Atlantic Period), peat bogs began to grow. Ombrogenous bogs (vegetation that obtains its nutrients primarily from rainwater rather than the bedrock) began to build up. The key factor was the water logging of the soil - only acid loving plants like heather, cotton grass and bog mosses (sphagnum *sp.*) could survive. The peat blanket gradually thickened, although the patterns and rates of growth were complex and irregular. In more recent times erosion of the peat has become a factor. Tarn pools now lie in this peat blanket and hence must post date its accumulation. How and when these features formed is a very complex problem.

The summit plateau of Dufton Fell lies between 660m and 690m above sea level (Figure 111). The peat blanket is everywhere around 2m thick, slightly more in slight depressions. It lies on flat lying Carboniferous sandstones of the Upper Alston Group. Cut into the peat are three named tarns - Great Rundale Tarn, Seamore Tarn and Little Rundale Tarn, a large unnamed tarn to the south, plus a myriad of smaller irregular pools of varying sizes and shapes. The current 1:25,000 Ordnance Survey maps show 46 other pools, but a walk across this area (which is not easy) shows far more unrecorded features. On the flat fell top just to north of this area there are nearly 20 others. Great Rundale and Seamore Tarns drain away eastwards. Little Rundale Tarn drains westwards. Most of the other pools have no direct outlets.

A very complex array of climatic, hydrological and biotic processes are at work here. Looking at these tarns and pools today they appear to be enlarging. Peat is a soft, fairly easily eroded material. The vertical banks of the tarns collapse relatively easily as demonstrated by detached lumps of peat and sods of the vegetation cover now lying on their fringes. There are a few places where the peat has been cut up by streams to form 'haggs' – noticeably for example around the head of Great Rundale Tarn and in the area at the extreme western end of Seamore Tarn. In very dry periods exposed peat can dry out on the surface and

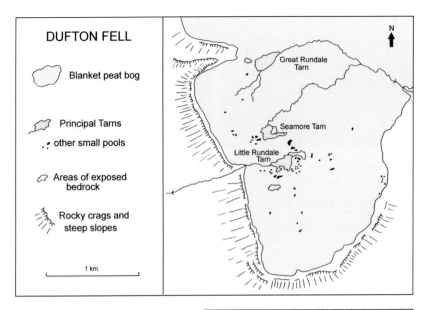

DUFTON FELL

Blanket peat bog

Principal Tarns

. ✦ other small pools

⟋ Areas of exposed
bedrock

Rocky crags and
steep slopes

1 km.

Great Rundale
Tarn

Seamore Tarn

Little Rundale
Tarn

N

Figure 111.
Above: Tarns on Dufton Fell.

Figure 112. Right: Typical peat depth
(approx 2m) in gully above Great
Rundale Tarn. Bedrock at base.

be deflated by wind action, particles
being carried away. Peat debris is
clearly in suspension in the inky
brown waters of the tarns and in the
streams that drain off this plateau. These pools are randomly distributed, which
seems to be typical of bogs on flat surfaces. Mire pools in many similar areas of
N.Europe where blanket bogs occur, particularly on sloping terrain, show
patterns in their spacing suggesting relationships between their form and the
processes of evolution. Most pools systems seem to originate only after a thick
layer of peat has accumulated. The pools may originate in small depressions, flat
areas or hollows where the plant cover has perished due to rising water tables. A
key biotic factor appears to be different rates of decomposition and reduced rates
of peat growth where surface water collects. Pools are in a constant state of flux
as peat is lost by decomposition and repositioning by water movements. A
further striking feature on Dufton Fell is the close proximity of pools where the
water is standing at quite different heights, suggesting complex lateral
movements of water through the peat. The peat has been completely stripped
away revealing the sandstone bedrock in a few places – notably at the eastern end
of Little Rundale Tarn and in the bay on the east side of Seamore Tarn.

Figure 113.
Tarns and pools on Dufton Fell

Above left: Great Rundale Tarn.

Above right: Seamore Tarn. The
tarn is in extreme distance, most
of tarn bed is dry with extensive
stretches of peat exposed to
wind erosion

Right: Little Rundale Tarn.
Detached tussocks of vegetation
and peat lumps exposed on
shore. Cotton grass in flower on
peat in foreground. Exposed sandstone bedrock on far shore of tarn.

Left: Series of
unnamed pools in area
south of Little Rundale.
The water is standing
at slightly different
heights in the different
pools

Below left and right:
typical small, often
irregular pools, in the
peat surface in the
south of the area.

8. TARNS ON LIMESTONE

Limestone is a soluble and permeable rock. A consequence of this is that areas of limestone topography tend to have an absence of surface drainage, most of the stream systems and drainage routes being below ground. Tarns and pools resting on limestone areas are therefore generally not to be expected.

Carboniferous Limestones outcrop fairly widely around the edges of the Lakeland fells. A narrow belt almost encircles the northern fells round from Egremont on the west to Cockermouth and Caldbeck. It then widens as it runs south eastwards to form the high limestone plateaux around Orton and Kirkby Stephen. In south Lakeland faulting in the rocks has created a series of prominent blocks of upstanding limestone. Scattered across these distinctive landscapes are in fact a number of interesting tarns and pools. Two particular geological factors account for this apparent anomaly. Many stretches of the limestones carry a cover of glacial debris - boulder clays, sands and gravels and glacial outwash material, which has allowed surface drainage to survive. Secondly, within the limestones in the south, there are thin, impermeable beds of shales, which create perched water tables, holding up the natural flow of water through the strata.

Bright Tarn, lies on Greystoke Moor, west of Penrith on the northern outcrop of the limestones. It is an area of very gently dipping Asbian Limestone with a thin cover of glacial boulder clay. The area which has little relief has seen some alterations to the natural drainage, as this is now enclosed agricultural land. The tarn is in a very open depression and is one of several hollows in the area that hold water. The peculiar pond feature of Blind Keld and some adjoining ponds lie about 1km to the west. South of the tarn is a similar large wet depression which is now practically dry. In the woods to the south west is a large diamond shaped pond with a tree covered island in it (an artificial creation). There are a series of swallow holes in the limestone surface round the southern fringes of the tarn – there is evidence that these may have been used at some stage in an abortive attempt to drain the tarn. The tarn itself is around 5m deep, but it often dries out.

Figure 114. Right above: Bright Tarn. This view is no longer visible. The tarn is now surrounded by woodland and is on private agricultural land with no public access.

The high limestone plateaux of the Orton and Asby areas contain some classic stretches of limestone terrain – great expanses of bare limestone pavements, dry valleys and bare limestone scars. Within them, however, rests Sunbiggin Tarn, Cow Dub and a number of other pools and depressions in the dimpled surfaces. Again the reasons for water being retained here is the cover of boulder clay left by the ice. A layer of blue-grey clay, hard and strong, was proved on the floor of Sunbiggin Tarn by coring. A layer of calcareous tufa, up to 5m thick, lies on top of the clay. The tarn is about 225m long and 180m across. The irregular Cow Dub pool, (200m x 50m in size), immediately to the south, is really part of the same feature. The whole area is an important ecological site, with significant aquatic plant communities in the tarns and on the surrounding valley mires, rich fens and hillside flushes. The water in the tarn is relatively shallow, nearly everywhere less than 3m in depth, but on the western side there is a steep depression where the water drops to almost 11m.

Figure 115. Sunbiggin Tarn looking south with the Howgill Fells on the skyline.

North of the tarn Seavy Dub and Spear Pots are two small pools in clay floored pits in the limestone surface. Both contain dense stands of vegetation with only patches of open water. Nearby are four other small unnamed wet pools and well to the north east of them is the similar feature of Asket Dub (Figure 116).

Figure 116. Left: Spear Pots, filled with vegetation and fringed with trees.
Right: Asket Dub, a minute tarn in a deep pit in the limestone.

Further to the east the limestone plateaux east of Ravenstonedale and to the south of Kirkby Stephen, are also heavily covered with glacial boulder clays. As a consequence there are several areas where the drainage is impeded, with mosses and mires on the surface. This is particularly the case around Tarn Mire (NY 756034) and Heckwith Mire (NY 750025). On Tarn Mire there is sizeable tarn – it now has a dam at its western end and stands higher than its natural level, but it illustrates the impact of the covering of impervious glacial materials. Two very distinct drumlin mounds of glacial clays form the northern shores of the tarn. (Figure 117).

Figure 117. Tarnmire Tarn, seen from the north side, with Wild Boar Fell on the skyline.

West of Ravenstonedale village, Hag Mire (NY 715054) is an artificial tarn, but again its construction in this area was only possible because of the impervious boulder clays. There is also Greenside Tarn (NY715035) – this however, lies just off the limestones, (actually on the Silurian sedimentary rocks), but it is again in these rather wet lowland areas floored with glacial debris. It shows some evidence of man-made alterations.

Figure 118.
Greenside Tarn, seen from south eastern end.

On the upstanding limestone scarp feature of Whitbarrow Scar, between the Lyth and Winster valleys south of Kendal there are two small, but interesting tarn features that are the result of the water tables in the rock being perched. Argles Tarn and Toby Tarn are both tucked away amongst the limestone scars and pavements of the Urswick Limestone high on the top of this ridge. Argles Tarn is in a deep strike aligned hollow. The limestones dip eastwards with prominent rocky scars running along the east side of the tarn. The water in the tarn is everywhere very shallow and much of it is choked with sedges and other vegetation. A 5-6m bed of black impervious Woodbine shale lies in the limestones beneath, and maintains the water level in the tarn A spring wells up in the water at the northern end. Some way to the north of Argles is the larger feature of Toby Tarn. This is almost rectangular, now around 90% filled up with vegetation, but with narrow strips of water fed by springs along its eastern and western edges. Again the water levels are retained by the presence of the Woodbine shales in the underlying rock.

Figure 119. Left: Argles Tarn, seen from the northern end where spring emerges. Right: Toby Tarn, looking S. Post in front of tarn is approx 2m high and gives scale.

North east of Whitbarrow Scar is the almost identical scar feature of Scout Scar and its northern extension Cunswick Scar. At the foot of Cunswick scar at around 130m elevation is Cunswick Tarn, an oval basin about 3m deep fed by springs. Wetland to both the north and south of the tarn indicates it was once a much longer feature. This is clearly a calcareous tarn, rich in aquatic and fen plants that thrive in the nutrient rich conditions. It is very difficult to be certain about the geological setting. Martin Limestones lie beneath the tarn and the Dalton Beds (again limestone), form the steep slopes along its eastern side. There are, however, considerable amounts of glacial debris around this relatively low lying area at the foot of the scarp. A distinct drumlin feature confines the tarn on its western side. The short outlet stream from its northern end seems to peter out.

The Carboniferous Limestones in the Furness Peninsula also tend to be lightly covered with boulder clays and glacial outwash deposits, but sufficient for a number of tarns to remain as surface features. The area has however been mineralised with hematite iron deposits and their exploitation has had a profound impact both on the surface topography and the drainage. Urswick Tarn is the largest of the tarns of Furness and is situated in a shallow boulder clay hollow on the Urswick Limestone. It is a picturesque tarn, nutrient rich and surrounded by the village of Great Urswick on three sides and wet meadow land at the southern outlet end. It is just over 12m deep in the centre and its waters are noticeably discoloured with hematite which washes in from the surrounding land.

Figure 120.

Left: Urswick Tarn from southern end.

Below: Holme Flat tarns.

In the irregular boulder clay ground on its south western side Little Urswick Tarn and Kirk Flatt are small depressional tarn features, the latter now virtually permanently dry. Holme Flat, in the meadows to the south however still retains water. 3kms west of Great Urswick, on the Dalton

Beds outcrop is Standing Tarn. This is a strange feature that strikingly fluctuates in level very widely, and appears not to be in its completely natural state.

Figure 121. Standing Tarn. The water is at a relatively low level, the bare exposed shoreline areas are clearly visible.

Further south west, Mereside Tarn, between the villages of Gleaston and Scales, is in a different situation. A heavy glacial drift cover in the area, much of it shaped into drumlins covers the underlying Gleaston Formation and Urswick Limestones. The triangular shaped tarn nestles in a hollow between drumlins. The water is very shallow, with clearly visible concentric bands in the hydrosere vegetation communities right around its fringes.

93

9. THE LOWLANDS

There are well over a hundred tarns and small pools on the lowlands that surround the upland areas of Lakeland. The outstanding feature of these areas is that they are almost completely covered with the glacial debris that the ice left behind as it melted and downwasted in the final stages of the last glacial episode. Bedrock does not figure in any significant way over the wide floor of the Eden valley in the east, over the vast plains of the Solway in the north, on the lowlands along the W. Cumbrian coast or in the flat lands of the lower valleys that run down to Morecambe Bay in the south. Stiff glacial boulder clays, outwash sands and gravels and river alluvium blanket virtually all of the low ground, in places to a considerable depth. The ice sheets that moved over the lowlands and eventually wasted away on them were however, a dynamic force. The ice was perpetually moving, with fast flowing ice streams constantly switching direction. Ice flows from Scotland and the Irish Sea were competing with Lakeland and Pennine ice, ebbing and flowing across this terrain. Thick layers of clay were plastered across the lowland landscapes, and in places shaped up into drumlins and ice moulded features. Huge quantities of meltwater were created. These carried sands, gravels and outwash debris onto the lowlands. The meltwaters were also erosive forces, cutting the glacial deposits and eroding into the bedrock on the flanks of the hills. The ice fronts oscillated back and forth leaving their mark with debris trails. The result was a very varied lowland terrain. It is impossible to describe all the tarn and pool features left behind, many are small and insignificant. On the other hand some quite large and distinctive tarns and groups of features remain. The main groups are highlighted in the following sections. The lowlands are now for the most part settled and used for agriculture. Some of the natural landforms have been modified by man. It is here also that many artificial water bodies have been created and many of the natural tarns and pools changed and enlarged for other uses.

KETTLE HOLES

A great number of the lowland tarns lie in kettle holes. These are depressions and enclosed hollows in the glacial deposits formed by the melt out of buried ice. Figure 122 illustrates the three common types of ice masses that were left in the glaciofluvial deposits in the final stages of the decay of the ice sheets. The resulting depressions tend to be fairly small and often occur in groups. The best examples are on the coastal strip of SW Cumbria around Nethertown and Braystones (Figure 123). Here at a very late stage of the glacial episode meltwater and ice from the Irish Sea pushed onto the coastal strip, covering the low ground with spreads of stratified sands and gravels, amongst which were decaying blocks of ice. This stretch of country is now

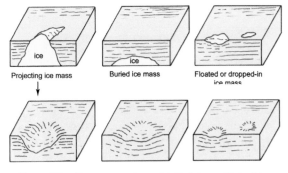

Figure 122.   Three common types of kettle holes and their origin

pitted with depressions. Braystones Tarn is the largest remaining feature. The large Sellafield Tarn has now been drained and the land developed. Most of the others are quite small, typically circular and forming enclosed depressions. The water retained in them tends to be shallow, consequently a large number now have peat and wetland vegetation in them, or have dried out completely.

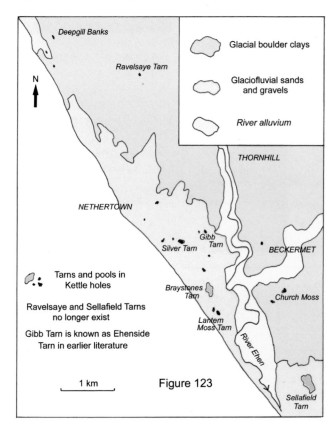

95

Figure 124.
Kettle holes
around
Braystones

Left: Braystones
Tarn. The largest
of the remaining
tarns, a very
shallow feature.
View from south
end.

Right: An unnamed kettle close to Silver
Tarn. An almost perfectly symmetrical
basin, now in agricultural land.

Left: Silver Tarn, now choked with
vegetation.

Right: Unamed
kettle close to
Silver Tarn.
View looking
south.
Towers of the
Sellafield
Nuclear plant
on skyline.

Left:
Church
Moss.

Elsewhere on the western Solway lowlands and along the narrow coastal strip down the west coast there are several other excellent examples of quite large kettle hole tarns. Martin Tarn, just west of Carlisle has been mentioned already in Chapter 7. Just inland from Mawbray there is a classic example at Tarns Dub. This is an almost circular tarn, 150m across, fringed with wetland, with an adjoining wetland area at the western side. There are other clear kettles in the same area, but now most are filled with peat mosses. To the south of Cockermouth, at the foot of the Ennerdale fells there is Mockerkin Tarn (Figure 125), another classic kettle feature. A belt of **kame** topography (similar to the landforms in the Brampton area - see later section) was built here at the edge of the wasting ice sheet banked against the fells to the east. The tarn must have been the site of a very large decaying block of ice. Around it, flat topped banks of glaciofluvial sands and gravels lie on the hillsides. Curving around the southern flanks of the tarn is an elongated ridge of sands – an **'esker'** feature – the remains of the infilling of a tunnel cut by meltwaters running westwards either in or under the ice. The tarn is a gentle oval shape, the curve of the esker forming its southern shores. It is 3.5m deep.

Figure 125. Mockerkin Tarn looking south. The esker ridge (with trees on it) form the far shore of the tarn. Ennerdale fells to left.

Much further south westwards along the coastal plain south of Eskmeals as far as Silecroft and Kirksanton, below the slopes of Black Combe, there is another narrow strip of pitted terrain. Here again Irish Sea ice pushed on to this land from the west. There are several small kettle hole tarns, most of them unnamed features. West of Bootle is Inmans Tarn, a further tarn at Gutterby and two small tarns to the south near Summer Hill. The largest feature is Barfield Tarn. This is a nutrient rich, oval shaped tarn with classic wetland fringes and stands of reedswamps around its western and southern shores. The kettle feature is larger than the tarn, steep banks of glacial material stand back from the tarn on the south side and there is a wooded area within the kettle on the north eastern side. The water in the tarn is now 4m deep.

Figure 126. Barfield Tarn seen from the south. The wooded part of the kettle is on the far side of the tarn.

THE BRAMPTON KAME BELT

In the extreme north east, banked against the northern end of the Pennines, is a stretch of very distinctive ground known as the Brampton Kame Belt. Kames are composed of glaciofluvial sands and gravel deposited by melting ice where it rests against a hillside slope. The Brampton kame is a large feature covering 40km² and extending from the Irthing valley just north of Brampton, southwards as far as Cumwhitton and Newbiggin (NY 560490). It is a terrace feature, the top of which stands mostly between 120 and 150m, with a few parts of it forming distinct flat topped hills. Contained within this belt is Talkin Tarn, along with some smaller tarns and pools notably at Boat House and North Scales and in the Carlatten area of the southern part of the kame (Figure 128).

Three distinctive landforms are found on the kame surface. First a series of depressions which are interpreted as kettle holes - these contain Talkin and the other tarns. Many of the other depressions no longer contain water, but remain as pits in the surface. Second, the surface of the kame has a series of ridges running across it. These represent former channels that were cut under the ice (subglacially), within the ice (englacially) or on top of the ice(supra-glacially) (Figure 127).Meltwater carried sand and gravel through these tunnels and channels - all of these materials now lie strewn over the present surface of the

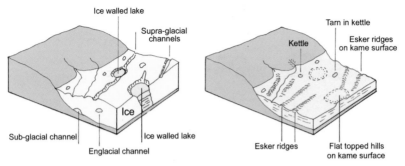

Figure 127.   Formation of Kame, during glaciation (left), after (right).

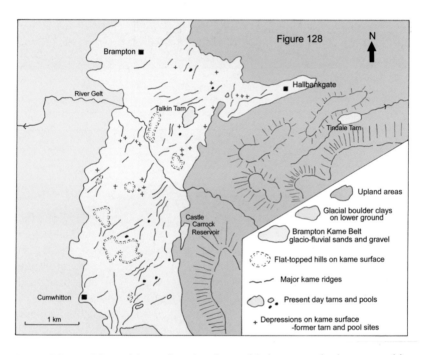

kame. Many of these ridges of sand and gravel help to contain the tarns – this is particularly the case with the ridges around the area of Talkin Tarn. The third features are the flat topped areas in the central part of the kame which are remnants of ice walled lakes that existed in the surface of the pitted ice sheet (Figure 127).There has thus been an almost total inversion of the topography – the low spots on the ice surface are now the highest parts of the kame deposits. Talkin Tarn has an area of around 26 ha. It lies in a conical like pit dropping to 11.8m close to its centre. Springs on the floor of the tarn feed it with water. There are noticeable ridges enclosing the tarn around its southern and western edges. (Figure 129).

Figure 129. Talkin Tarn.
Above: View across tarn towards the sandy ridges around the southern shore.
Below: The western shore.

TINDALE TARN

Tindale Tarn is not related to the Brampton Kame but as figure 128 shows it lies in a shallow valley that cuts eastwards through the Carboniferous gritstones and coal measure rocks of this north-west corner of the Pennine upland. It stands at 222m. It is difficult to understand its origin. The eastward running valley may be an old course taken by the River Gelt pre-glacially. The river now has been diverted westwards and cuts across the Brampton Kame and eventually joins the Irthing and the Eden. Ice clearly went eastwards through this valley and eroded its floor. It was undoubtedly also a route taken by meltwaters draining eastwards into the South Tyne catchment. Boulder clay covers part of the valley floor. The tarn is now about 900 m long, but there is evidence that it was once longer and stood almost 2m higher than it is at present. It has suffered a series of alterations. The Tindale area was extensively mined for coal in the Nineteenth Century. Pit workings seem to have altered the water table levels and there are some suggestions that an unsuccessful attempt was made to drain it. The outlet stream has been straightened and deepened. Very recently the RSPB, who now mange the tarn for its bird populations, have modified some of the shore areas and created low islands towards the eastern end. 99% of the tarn is less than 3m deep, with one very small area reaching 4m deep towards the outlet end.

Figure 130. Tindale Tarn seen from the head end looking eastwards. The shallow ponds in the foreground mark the former extension of the tarn at its upper end.

TARNS IN GLACIAL MELTWATER CHANNELS

Very extensive networks of channels cut by meltwaters exist on the flanks of the lowlands and over the spreads of glacial debris over low ground. As we have seen with the Brampton Kame Belt meltwaters ran over, through, and under the ice sheets. When the ice finally melted away the channels were usually abandoned and consequently now have little reference to the patterns of present day surface streams. Many of these channels were cut by water under hydrostatic pressure, so they sometimes ran up hill or had distinct humps in their log profiles. In addition debris has often been left in their floors creating dips and hollows in which tarns have collected. The best examples are shown in figures 131 and 132 below. Many other channels, notably the Nannycatch, inland of Cleator Moor and its extension into Kirk Beck and Black Moss east of Egremont both contain old tarn beds. There are also pools in the floors of the Kinmont and Corney channels in the area inland from Bootle, below Black Combe.

Figure 131. Studgill Tarn, on the Pennine flanks at Keisley Bank, east of Dufton. Meltwaters flowed through the channel from right to left (ie northwards). The channel is now dry, apart from the tarn. It stands at about 300m and is cut into bedrock (tuffs of the Kirkland Formation) and is aligned along a fault line. (NY 715241)

Figure 132. An unnamed tarn in a deep meltwater channel at Low Trough, on the western flank of Murton Pike (NY 731225). Meltwaters went left to right through the channel out on to the low ground of the Eden valley. The channel is in solid rock.

TARNS IN DRUMLIN FIELDS

Many of the thick sheets of glacial till that the ice left plastered over the lowland areas of Cumbria were strongly moulded by the moving ice into swarms of drumlins - so called drumlin fields. These landscapes of smooth, oval-shaped or elliptical hills of bouldery glacial clays, orientated with the direction of flow of the ice frequently hold small tarns within the hollows between the individual drumlins. The largest spreads of this type of terrain are in the floor of the Eden Valley and across the Solway Plain, but the Whinfell-Grayrigg area in the south-east best illustrates small tarns in this setting (Figure 133). Skelsmergh Tarn, Whinfell Tarn and Grayrigg Tarn are the best examples, but there are several other smaller features in this area and many wetland hollows that mark the site of former tarns. Most are very shallow features with small catchments, often with few or any inlet or outlet streams. Characteristically they show floating and emergent vegetation around their wetland shores and are frequently fringed with carr woodland.

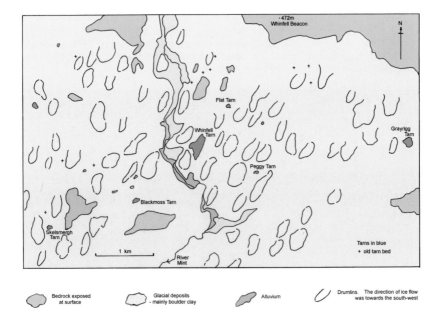

Figure 133.
Drumlin topography in the Whinfell – Grayrigg area.

Figure 134. The drumlin terrain around Peggy Tarn. View looking SW from above Grayrigg Hall. A gentle rolling landscape of rich pastureland. Peggy Tarn, a kidney-shaped, shallow tarn around 2.5m deep, fringed with fen and carr woodland, is concealed by the trees in the centre of the view

Figure 135. Whinfell Tarn, the largest of these tarns. The inflow is from springs only and the very narrow outflow ditch (<1m) flows visibly only in wet weather. The maximum depth of the tarn is only around 5m. It is surrounded by farmland and its water has a high pH of 8.0. Highly organic black mud covers the floor of the tarn. The view is from the SW shore. The outlet is to the right. Whinfell Beacon on the skyline

Figure 136.
Skelsmergh Tarn.
A beautiful, oval
tarn about 150m
across nestling
between steep
sided drumlins and
completely ringed
with fen and willow
carr. The water is
no more than 5m
deep, but on the
floor of the tarn
coring has revealed
several metres of
organic material,
with clays and

angular debris at the base which sludged into the basin from the unvegetated
slopes of the drumlins immediately after the ice had melted back.

Figure 137.
Infilled tarn
south of Otter
Bank, north of
Skelsmergh
Tarn.

This lies in the
same hollow
as Skelsmergh
Tarn. It is now
completely
colonised with
dense willow
woodland and
wetland
vegetation.

Figure 138.
Flat Tarn.
Open water now
covers little more
than 10% of this
shallow enclosed
basin. Wetland
and woodland
completely
surround it. The
tarn is barely 2m
deep.
View from the SW
with Whinfell
Beacon (472m) in
the distant view.

Figure 139.
Grayrigg Tarn.
The highest of this
group of tarns
standing close to
the moorland edge
at 224m. It has a
very open shallow
basin floored with
boulder clay. The
water is shallow,
only 2.5m at the
deepest point. It is
fringed with
wetland and was
once a much
larger sheet of
water.

Figure 140.
Blackmoss
Tarn.
A very shallow
(<2m)
triangular
shaped tarn,
with several
rushy islands
with alder
saplings. It is
in an area of
rich farmland
in a very
shallow basin.

Figure 141.
An unnamed
old tarn bed SE
of Crake Hall.
(SD 539975).

Very typical of
the shallow
basins in this
gently rolling
drumlin
topography.

There is a further area of lowland containing tarns in the extreme south east, well to the east of Kendal and stretching towards the valley of the river Lune (Figure 142). It is an irregular terrain mostly underlain by hard Silurian sedimentary rocks that dip gently southwards (at <25°). The rocks are cut by N-S running faults which imprint a lineation in that direction on the landforms. It is also partly covered with glacial boulder clays which are in places shaped up into drumlins. This has proved to be ideal terrain in which to create small reservoirs. Some of the water features shown on Figure 142 are either partly or wholly artificial – without very detailed local research it is difficult to ascertain their original form. Lily Mere and the large Killington Reservoir nestle within the dense drumlins in the north of the area. Both are largely artificial features, the reservoir supplying the nearby Lancaster Canal. Eskrigg Tarn is a natural feature in a classic inter drumlin situation. It has

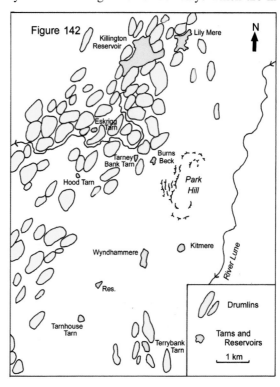

dense wetland vegetation around all its edges, reedbeds, alder carr and woodland. Hood Tarn is in agricultural land, but it remains a natural feature. It is shallow with water lilies around its fringes, patches of reeds and a narrow belt of mixed woodland around it. Tarneybank Tarn lies in a shallow boulder clay hollow and is progressively shrinking in size as the wetland and carr woodland encroach into it. Nearby to the east is Burns Beck Moss, no longer a tarn but now an important wetland nature reserve. There are two deep basins here eroded into the bedrock, the western section now filled with about 8m of peat and the eastern basin with about 6m. Kitmere, Wyndhammere and Tarnhouse Tarns are all reservoirs retained by masonry dams. In the extreme south east Terrybank Tarn is possibly a large kettle feature. Steep convex mounds of glacial material surround it. It has an outlet stream and stands of reeds and rushes at its upper end.

Figure 143. Tarneybank Tarn. View is looking NW. Tarn outlet at left.

Figure 144 Burns Beck Moss. This was once a sizeable tarn. It is now completely infilled with wetland vegetation. View is from Hill's Quarry at the north end.

Figure 145. Terrybank Tarn. View from the slopes of Tarn Hill at the southern end looking towards the head of the tarn.

10. TARNS ALONG THE COAST

Cumbria has an extremely long coastline, well over 250 kms depending on how accurately you take in all the irregularities and inlets. Most of it, (probably over 80%) is based on 'soft rocks' – glacial boulder clays, sands, gravels and unconsolidated sediments. Rocky cliffs and hard rocks at sea level are only found in the section from Maryport round to St Bees and in a few places in Morecambe Bay. For the rest, the coast is a patchwork of coastal mudflats, marshes, raised beaches and infilled estuarine lowlands. Sand and shingle has been generated and constantly moved into spits and ridges. Long stretches of sand dune habitats dominate much of the outer Solway and the western shores. Within this narrow belt there are tarns and pools to be found.

Grune Point, north of Silloth is a classic shingle spit feature, built by northerly drifting currents which have piled up ridges of shingle. The western seaward face is constantly being eroded and curved shingle ridges built and destroyed around its northern end. Within the heart of the feature, between the ridges, there is an extremely shallow, unnamed tarn, which constantly changes, rising and falling in this dynamic environment. (Figure 146 above)

Classic systems of sand dunes stretch between Mawbray and Allonby in the north, along the coast at Drigg, at Sandscale Haws on the western side of the Furness Peninsula north of Barrow, and along much of Walney Island. Dune systems are built by wind moving sand onshore. Successive belts of dunes may be progressively created and then moved gently inland until the mobile sand is stabilised by the growth of vegetation. Deflation creates 'blow outs' and linear depressions in areas of unstable, dry sand. Deflation can continue to remove sand from low lying areas until the low level of summer water tables is reached. Such low spot are termed 'slacks' and it is here water can collect and remain to produce small tarns and pools. The Mawbray and Allonby dunes show distinct linear slacks between the lines of dune that parallel the coast. There are a number of small pools here and several have been artificially modified to ensure water is maintained throughout the year as they can be very important wildlife sites. The Drigg and Sandscale Haws dunes are on a much larger scale and have many mature, vegetated dune systems and prominent slack pools. There are over 30 pools at Sandscale Haws and at least 20 at Drigg. Once the dune slacks become vegetated their pools are progressively encroached upon by plant growth. The pools have limited catchment areas and tend to be relatively short lived.

Figure 147. Pools in Dune slacks.
Right:An artificially modified pool in the Mawbray Dunes. Sites like this are important habitats for natterjack toads which are protected species, but flourish in this part of Cumbria.

Left: Typical dune slack pools in the dunes south of Allonby.

Right: One of the many pools in the Sandscale Haws dune system. The dunes here are stabilised by vegetation and the pools are steadily infilling with sedges and other plants.

HELTON TARN

At first sight it would seem that this tarn is not a coastal feature, but once you look into its somewhat complex history it become clear that is intimately tied up with recent changes in sea level. It lies on the flat floor of the Winster valley, now at least 6 kms inland. The Winster is one of the principal infilled estuary areas of S.Lakeland (Figure 148). Investigations in the late 1950's used cores to probe the sediments on the bottom of the tarn and across the valley floor. These showed that the sea, standing at a much higher level in the past had flooded up into the Winster valley and up into the Kent valley to the east. It had stood at approximately +6m above present levels and had extended up into the Winster valley at least 4 kms further north than the present tarn. Helton Tarn is a *remanié* of this event. At present the tarn is less than 200m long, the water is very shallow and there is extensive wetland around it, particularly on its eastern and southern sides.

Coring into the sediments around the tarn show there is a deep rock basin here cut by glaciers into the hard bedrock of the Bannisdale Formation. A tarn (or probably small lake) must have existed here in the post glacial period. Just over 1 km down valley of the present tarn, there is rocky bar of these Bannisdale rocks running right across the valley floor at Bleacrag.

The original lake was held up by this bar. The sediments on the floor of the basin are typical of those found on the floors of many small lakes and tarns indicating freshwater conditions and the gradual accumulation of debris being washed in from the surrounding landscape. On the top of these freshwater deposits however, are around 10m of laminated silts and clays that are marine in origin. These indicate that the sea, standing at +6m above its present level had managed to overtop the rocky bar at Bleacrag and extend high up into the Winster valley bringing with it an infill of marine debris. Dating of the deposits show this occurred around 6000 BP in the Atlantic Period of post glacial time. Since that time as the sea receded, water levels in the Helton Tarn basin have been controlled by the Bleacrag rock bar. A

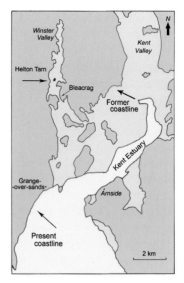

Figure 148: shows the present and former shore lines in the Winster and Kent estuaries).

sizeable lake probably existed in the area above the rock bar well into historical times. Material continued to collect on the valley floor with the washing in of stream sediments and the progressive growth of fen vegetation; the lake gradually shrinking in size. Man has also intervened more recently. The river channel through the rock bar has been deepened and straightened, helping the land around the tarn to drain and the old lake floor to be taken into agricultural use.

Figure 149. Helton Tarn

Above The Helton Tarn valley seen from the Hare Hill ridge to the west - looking east with the Carboniferous limestone scar of Yewbarrow behind. The tarn is just visible in the centre of the picture.

Right: The southern end of Helton Tarn. Wooded slopes of Yewbarrow behind.

11. THE MAN-MADE LAKES AND TARNS

In this concluding chapter brief reference to a few of the man-made lakes and tarns in the landscape must be made. As we have seen back in Chapter 1 there are well over 300 small lakes, tarns and pools that have been created by man's activities over the last 200-300 years or so. Most of them are relatively small, some quite insignificant and many of them now abandoned and no longer fulfilling their original purpose. The majority were created by the construction of earth, concrete or masonry dams to provide water supply reservoirs or water for industrial uses. Large numbers were also created simply to provide ornamental landscape features, particularly in Victorian and Edwardian times. Others are the legacy of the extractive industries – sand, gravel, clay, stone and other minerals. All are now very much a part of this Lakeland landscape, many with interesting historical stories to tell. Many have matured and become attractive landscape features. The accompanying illustrations here illustrate just a few examples.

Figure 150. Left: Wet Sleddale Reservoir. This is a major water supply reservoir completed in 1966. The surprisingly 600m long dam was necessary because of the shallow nature of the valley. It is of concrete construction, 21m high. The water is piped from here into the nearby Haweswater valley.

Figure 151. Right: Blencarn Lake in the Eden Valley. An even more recent construction, used now as a popular fishing lake.

Figure 152.
Top left:
Lanty's Tarn.
An excellent
example of the
picturesque.
Although artificial,
it is a much
photographed
location set in an
area of now mature
woodland. The low
concrete dam is at
the far end and
nearby is an 'ice
house' built at the
same time as the
dam by the
Marshall family to
supply the nearby
'big house' at
Patterdale Hall.
Also an interesting
geological location
in a col feature that
cuts through the
Keldas ridge.

Figure 153.
Left: Goosey Foot
Tarn in Grizedale
Forest. One of the
many tarns in the
forest constructed
for wildlife interest.
Now a mature
feature in a
coniferous
woodland setting.

Figure 154. Above: Two very different examples of small tarns left by extractive activities.
Left: Kentmere Tarn, the flooded workings of the old diatomite diggings in the valley floor
of the Kentmere valley. Right: Arthuret Ponds, old gravel pits in the Esk valley, just south
west of Longtown in N. Cumbria. Now they are important ornithological sites.

GLOSSARY AND GUIDE TO SOME OF THE TERMS USED IN THE BOOK.

Ablation: – the process of wastage of ice by melting.

Areal scouring: – large scale erosion of bedrock by ice sheets.

Boulder clay: – an English term for **till.** **Till:** – a mixture of mud, sand, gravel and boulder size material deposited by glacier ice.

Cleavage: Planes in a rock, usually developed through intense deformation and pressure, along which it can be split into thin sheets (eg. as in slates).

Dates: BP (Before Present) using AD 1950 as base. Some dates for ice age events are shown as calibrated dates in thousands of years **(eg. 12.2-11.9 ka)**. Dating these events is a complex procedure. Calibrated dates do not equate exactly with calendar years. For more detail see booklet No. 3 in this series 'The Ice Age in the Lake District'.

Dip and Strike: Dip is the angle at which a bed of rock is inclined in relation to the horizontal. (diagram at right).

Strike is the direction at right angles to dip.

Geological Groups/Formations: All the different rocks in Lakeland are grouped (according to their age) into Groups/Supergroups, Formations and Members, and most bear local names. These have been used in the text and follow the names used by British Geological Survey (BGS) on their maps and in their publications. For more details of this in terms of Lakeland, see booklet No. 4 in this series 'Lakeland Rocks: an Introductory Guide'.

Glacial erratic: large pebbles/cobbles/boulders transported from their source by ice.

Ice sheet: – a mass of ice of considerable thickness and covering a large area.(eg. over the whole of Lakeland).

Ice stream: part of an ice sheet in which the ice flows more rapidly.

Kame: (gaelic word) – a steep sided hill of sand and gravel deposited adjacent to a glacier margin.

Esker: (gaelic word) – a long, often sinuous ridge of sand and gravel deposited by a stream in a subglacial tunnel.

Openwork boulders: loose boulders piled together with no matrix material in the spaces.

Perched water table: a water table that is held at unusually high levels because of an impermeable rock layer.

Pitted plain: – a plain of glaciofluvial sediment with depressions (kettles) resulting from melting of buried ice blocks

Ribbon lake: – a long, narrow lake resulting from glacial erosion.

Piedmont lake: – an alternative name for a ribbon lake.

Roche(s) moutonnée(s): An upstanding outcrop of bedrock shaped by a glacier flowing over it: rounded and smooth on upstream side and top; craggy and plucked on downstream side.

Tear fault: – a fault where movement is predominantly horizontal.

FURTHER READING

1. Elizabeth Howarth, George de Boer, Ian Evans, Henry Osmaston, Winifred Pennington, Alan Smith, Philip Storey and Brian Ware, 2003. **Tarns of the Central Lake District.** Brathay Exploration Group Trust, Ambleside , Cumbria.. x + 204p.
   This is a comprehensive study of 50 tarns in the Central Lake District, with depth surveys and a series of chapters on the environmental context of these tarns. It is a very useful source of specialised material. The 50 tarns covered in this volume have been identified by asterisks * in the Index to the tarns in the present book.

2. W. Heaton Cooper 1959
   The Tarns of Lakeland. Frederick Warne & Co: London.
   Although this is quite an old work it is still a unique source of information on a large number of Lakeland tarns. As well as Heaton Cooper's delightful paintings, which are really the centre of the book, it has a great deal of detail about the tarns and is particularly strong on the historical aspects.

3. Peter Wilson. 2010.
   Lake District Mountain Landforms. Scotforth Books: Lancaster.
   This is the best and most authoritative book on the geomorphology of the Lake District. It is an easy to read and well illustrated account of the landforms and the processes involved in their evolution. In relation to the present book it gives excellent background material on the glacial processes that have shaped the Lakeland landscape.

4. Geoffrey Fryer. 1991.
   A Natural History of the Lakes, Tarns and Streams of the English Lake District. Freshwater Biological Association.
   A comprehensive volume on all aspects of the natural history of the lakes and tarns.

INDEX

Six figure National Grid map references are given against all the named lakes and tarns listed in the index below. An asterisk * is shown against all the lakes and tarns that are included in the Brathay Hall *'Tarns of the Central Lake District'* publication (see Further Reading list on previous page). A depth chart for all these lakes and tarns is available in that volume.

NY221084	Lambfoot Dub 70
NY317068	Lang How. 48
SD260885	Lang Tarn. 57
	Lank Rigg. 73
NY385163	Lanty's Tarn, 113
NY417018	Latrigg Tarn. 65
NY233150	Launchy Tarn. 47
SD291849	Leech Tarn. 56
SD280993	Levers Water.* 30
SD604915	Lily Mere. 107
	Limestone. 89
SD410953	Lindeth Tarn. 10
	Little Hart Crag. 74
NY309032	Little Langdale T.* 19
NY732271	Little Rundale Tarn. 80
SD266739	Little Urswick Tarn. 93
NY249338	Little Water. 78
NY509170	Littlewater Tarn. 69
NY241304	Lincomb Tarns. 43
NY302051	Lingmoor Tarn. 49
NY198130	Loaf Tarn. 46
SD291936	Long Moss.* 57
NY014127	Longlands Lake. 7
	Loughrigg Fell. 48
NY345043	Loughrigg Tarn.* 20
SD191995	Low Birker Tarn. 52
	Lowland mosses. 85
	Low Rigg. 40
NY162094	Low Tarn.* 52
NY731225	Low Trough. 102
SD275983	LowWater(Coniston).* 31
	Maiden Moor. 74
	Man-made tarns, 112
	Martcrag Moor. 48
NY258516	Martin Tarn. 85
	Mawbray. 109
	Meathop Moss. 85
	Meltwater channels. 101
SD267718	Mereside Tarn. 93
	Middleboot Knotts. 71
NY397011	Middlerigg Tarn. 65
NY083232	Mockerkin Tarn. 97
NY364029	Mortimere. 60

	Mosedale (Wasdale). 76
	Murton. 102
	Nannycatch. 102
NX990075	Nethertown. 94
NY249338	Nevin Tarn. 78
SD408827	Newton Tarn. 68
	Orton. 90
	Oulton Moss. 85.
NY252350	Overwater. 77
NY681254	Parl Tarn. 10
	Peat. 85
SD569976	Peggy Tarn 104
	Place Fell. 40
SD494989	Potter Tarn. 66
NY203043	Quagrigg Moss. 74
SD485959	Ratherheath Tarn. 67
NX990099	RavelsayeTarn.9, 95
NY396087	Red Screes. 72
NY348153	Red Tarn (Helv).* 6,9,31
NY268037	Red T. (Wrynose).* 49
	Riggindale. 72
	Rise Fell. 85
	Robinson. 72
SD287847	Roerigg Tarn. 56
	Rossett Pike. 48
SD332824	Roudsea Tarn. 65
NY495194	Rough Hill Tarn. 69
NY220081	Round How Tarn. 71
SD511992	Routen Beck Tarn. 66
NY085452	Salta Moss. 85
NY755989	Sand Tarn. 81
	Sandscale Haws. 109
NY385098	Scandale Tarn. 64
NY519152	Scalebarrow Tarn. 69
NY430635	Scaleby Moss. 85
NY329281	Scales Tarn.* 31
SD428972	School Knott Tarn.* 57
NY160104	Scoat Tarn.* 32
NY730275	Seamore Tarn. 86

	Seathwaite Fell. 44
SD253988	Seathwaite Tarn.* 8,9,18
NY022042	Sellafield Tarn. 9, 95
	Sergeant Man. 48
	Sheffield Pike. 69
	Silver How. 48
NX999068	Silver Tarn. 96
NY162011	Siney Tarn.* 51
Ny480034	Skeggles Water. 57, 64
SD534967	Skelsmergh Tarn. 103
NY356030	Slew Tarn. 60
NY455100	Small Water. *33
NY296211	Snipeshow Tarn. 42
SD401879	Sow How Tarn. 68
NY228091	Sprinkling Tarn.* 32, 45
SD242744	Standing Tarn. 93
NY308112	Steel Fell. 48
NY287077	Stickle Tarn.* 29
SD214928	Stickle T. (Duddon).55
NY199025	Stony Tarn. *50
	Stony Cove Pike. 73
NY716241	Studgill Tarn. 102
NY222099	Styehead Tarn. *43
NY677077	Sunbiggin Tarn. 90
	Swarth Fell. 83
	Swindale. 69

SD505994	Taggleshaw Tarns. 66
NY545590	Talkin Tarn. 89
NY116474	Tarn Dubs. 97
NY258123	Tarn at Leaves.* 43
	Tarn Crags. 48
	Tarn Hill. 55
NY331000	Tarn Hows. 9, 60
SD572833	Tarnhouse Tarn. 102
NY753032	Tarnmire Tarn. 91
SD588881	Tarney Bank Tarn. 107
SD592825	Terrybank Tarn. 107
NY304236	Tewit Tarn. 41
NY146118	Tewit How Tarn. 41
NY248060	Three Tarns (B/fell). 74
	Threlkeld Knotts. 83
	Thunacar Knott. 48
NY605585	Tindale Tarn. 100

SD445880	Toby Tarn. 91
SD414818	Tom Tarn. 68
	Torver. 56
SD281926	Torver Tarn.* 58
NY128053	Tosh Tarn. 52
SD270745	Urswick Tarn. 93
	Wasdale. 52
NY275161	Watendlath Tarn.* 22
NY550114	Wet Sleddale R. 10, 112
SD331988	Wharton Tarn. 60
	Whernside. 85
SD559980	Whinfell Tarn. 103
	Whin Rigg. 72, 75
	Wild Boar Fell. 81, 85
	Winster Valley. 110
NY136043	Woodhow Tarn. 52
SD328918	Wood Moss Tarn. 62
SD592850	Wyndhammere. 107
NY322004	Yew Tree Tarn. 9, 60
NY317068	Youdell Tarns. 49

FINALE

All of these smaller lakes and tarns are ephemeral.
Ultimately, under present environmental conditions they will infill with sediment, become wetlands and then eventually dry out leaving flat infilled lake and tarn basins.
This has already happened here at White Moss (centre of picture above) – now a wet lowland moss (partly wooded) in the Glenderamackin valley, near Mungrisedale, in north-east Lakeland. The view is from Eycott Hill looking north-west. Carrock Fell is in the far distance on the right, Bowscale Fell to the left.

THE AUTHOR

Dr Alan Smith is now retired from an academic career. He has written several books, papers and guides on Lakeland Geology and Geomorphology. He is a past President and General Secretary of the Cumberland Geological Society. He lives in Keswick.
All the maps and diagrams have been compiled and drawn by the author. All the photographs are also by the author.

COVER PHOTOGRAPHS

Front cover: Greendale Tarn – view from the head of the tarn with slopes of Middle Fell to the left.
Back cover :   Upper: Watendath Tarn from Rough Knott.
Lower: Blea Water from High Street.